*Merrily
We Sing*

Merrily We Sing

105 Polish Folksongs

♪

Collected and Edited by Harriet M. Pawlowska
With an Analysis of the Music by
Grace L. Engel

♪

Foreword by
Emelyn Elizabeth Gardner

DETROIT - *Wayne State University Press* - 1961

Publication of *Merrily We Sing* was made possible through financial assistance of the Ford Foundation and the Wayne State University Publications Fund for Polish Culture and History.

To
Emelyn Elizabeth Gardner

Foreword

SINCE the founding of the American Folklore Society, January 4, 1888, there has been a steadily growing interest in the subject of folksong on the part of many great scholars in this country. One of the first of these was Professor Francis James Child of Harvard University, whose famed collection of 305 English and Scottish popular ballads was published in five volumes (1892-98). Many of these ballads were brought to this country, mainly from the countries of their origin, through the memories and singing of them by early American settlers from England and Scotland. Today an enormous collection of these ballads with their tunes, which were omitted by Child, and in many widely varied versions of both tunes and words are in process of publication through the distinguished scholarship of Professor Bertrand H. Bronson of the University of California at Berkeley.

While a folk ballad tells a story in song, a folksong is generally so informal that any story element it may possess is negligible. Story may be altogether lacking. Otherwise the two forms have much in common. Both products of an earlier time came to this country in the memories and on the lips of emigrants from their homelands to America. Both types are of unknown authorship and date of origin. In common with similar songs from any country, Polish folksongs are unstable in content, partly owing to lapses in memory on the part of singers and partly to their desire to adapt songs to changed conditions and personnel. As a folksong may have no story to direct it, almost any change may occur in it during the course of time except an identifying spark of the national spirit of the people who created it.

Instead of being integrated wholes, folksongs are waifs and strays of traditional song —echoes as it were of the joys and sorrows, the work and play, the hope and despair of the simple people who originated them and preserved them in their memories. In Detroit today such songs are most likely to be heard at Polish social gatherings, like holiday feasts, weddings, dances, and merrymakings of various kinds, which recall bygone days when folksongs filled the place now enlivened by radio and TV productions. Older people, upon request, are happy to sing for interested listeners the folksongs which they still recall and enjoy.

Miss Harriet Pawlowska, a former graduate student of Wayne State University, was one of those who thought the old time folksongs of Poland were worth collecting and offering as part fulfillment of the requirements for her M.A. degree in English at Wayne State University. As she knew the tune is the heart-throb of a folksong, she invited her friend, Miss Grace Engel, an excellent teacher of music in the Detroit schools, well prepared for the work of transcribing the recorded music, to cooperate with her in obtaining the tunes of the songs. This they did through the help of a recording machine kindly lent for the purpose by the Dictaphone Company of

America. Miss Engel wrote the tune from the record and Miss Pawlowska translated the Polish words into simple English which fitted the tunes.

Although such songs are slight in content, it was decided at the 1958 annual meeting of the American Folklore Society that they in common with other forms of folklore were important reservoirs of matter helpful to anthropologists, ethnologists, historians, writers of prose and verse, musicologists and performers in song and dance. One anthropologist present even went so far as to advocate that the literary and musical content of folksongs be replaced by study of them as socio-historical documents.

In his closing remarks at this meeting, the retiring president of the society, Professor Wayland D. Hand of the University of California, maintained that the rich ethnic folklore of our great cities was a natural resource and recommended the formation of a national commission of folk culture.

Among the many ethnic groups which hold a place of distinction in Detroit the Polish people are outstanding. And it is logical to assume that this collection of their folksongs will be favored with a niche already reserved for similar matter in the Archives of Folksong in the Congressional Library in Washington.

Emelyn E. Gardner
Professor Emeritus, Wayne State University
Claremont, California.

Preface

THE United States is unique among nations. Founded by a homogeneous group, it has attracted individuals from the heterogeneous world, who from the beginning eagerly have sought its shores and its material prosperity.

That in itself is not unique, for it is natural for man to strive for material improvement. But when the migrating millions want to become an integral part of the attracting nation, that is unique. It is unique, moreover, because in each individual exists a relentless urge to express himself in terms of the roots of his culture. When a nation of individuals fuses the old world of their cradle with the new world facing them, that is unique.

It may have been the vastness of the American territory which encouraged the free play of individuals that brought the millions here. The Gargantuan task facing the new nation at the beginning may have led it to bypass differences which characterize all peoples and to concentrate on those qualities which are common to all men. The direct cause, however, is the essence of the fundamental documents of the United States, which recognize the dignity of the individual. As a result, the people of all nations have embellished the tapestry of this nation into a design of infinite variety, without changing the fiber or weakening the fabric. No nation in the world can claim direct affinity with the United States because of the preponderance of the cultural ties of its emigrants. The term *American* suggests relationship but repels direct kinship.

It is in the spirit of free play and freedom of expression that the folksongs of Poland have been preserved in the United States. The present collection, gathered in Detroit under the auspices of Wayne State University, is offered as a symbol of the gifts to the United States from the people of Polish heritage. It is an offering from one area of their cultural wealth which Poles bring when they settle here and fuse with the other peoples of the world.

Although this collection contains only a portion of the Polish folksongs known in this country, it is representative of several important characteristics. The ballads, for instance, show the cultural kinship of the Poles with the people of western and eastern Europe as well as the British Isles. There is evidence of acculturation. One is aware of the creativity of the folksinger in the freedom with which he adapts or combines songs to please his mood. As might be expected, the songs give evidence of text corruption, revisions wrought by changes in mores and faults of memory. And they demonstrate the melodic beauty of Polish song, variety in textual pattern, as well as the Polish idiom in music and ethnology.

It may be that in years to come, one of these preserved melodies will be part of the character of the American folksong. It is hoped that American composers of the future will feel in these songs the pulse of America and incorporate some of them into the themes of serious American music. When that occurs, another bright thread will have been added to the tapestry which is America.

Many persons have given invaluable aid in the making of this collection. My deepest gratitude goes to Professor Emeritus Emelyn E. Gardner, who inspired me to search for Polish folk material. I am grateful to Professors Alexander Brede and Thelma G. James for editorial assistance, and to Grace L. Engel for her patient help in checking the metrical English translations with the music.

I am indebted to the following persons who made available invaluable library material: Gordon W. Thayer and Walter F. Vella, former and present curators, respectively, of the John G. White Collection of Folklore and Orientalia of the Cleveland Public Library; the late Miecislaus Haiman, curator of the Archives and Museum of the Polish Roman Catholic Union of America, Chicago; the late Msgr. Wladyslaus Krzyzosiak, rector, and the Rev. Andrew Pawelczak, formerly librarian, of SS. Cyril and Methodius Seminary, Orchard Lake, Michigan; Professor Bruno Stefan, St. Mary's College, Orchard Lake, Michigan; Dr. Harold Spivake, Chief of the Division of Music, the Library of Congress; and Miss Sophia Wolczynska, formerly of the Department of Foreign Languages, and the staff of the Reference Department, Detroit Public Library.

For reading and checking the Polish texts of the songs in the early stages of the study, I am under obligation to Mrs. May Czajkowa, Mr. Thaddeus Maychrzycki, and Dr. Edmund Ordon.

For the use of the dictaphone and the recorder, I wish to thank the American Dictaphone Company and the Library of Congress, respectively.

Finally, to those people who sang their Polish folksongs into the dictaphone and then patiently dictated the texts, I extend my deep appreciation.

H.M.P.

Comments on the Texts

How does a folksong collection begin? It may begin by way of a proverb. Proverbs in the oral tradition may be hard to find, but this is what the collector thinks she wants, so with perseverance she finds an informant or two. With such a beginning, she prods others and learns that people may not know proverbs, but they recognize a challenge. "Proverbs?" they say indifferently "No, but I know a tale or two— something from my grandmother's past." The collector takes what she can get and moves on. Like a street peddlar of old, she now calls, "Any proverbs? Any tales? Proverbs, tales I'll take. Have you any?" Her collection of proverbs grows, and to the tales she adds legends and—a singer or two whose eyes glow only when there is song in the air. So the collector comes back with a recorder, and the singer knows other singers, and the store soon is pleasantly burdened with an abundance of song. Thus was born this collection of Polish folksongs.

The purpose of this collection is twofold: to see to what extent the Polish folksong has been preserved by the Polish immigrant to Detroit and to acquaint the American music lover with the traditional melodies and themes of a people who comprise an integral part of America today. The study is based on field work as well as on such research as library facilities in this country permitted.

Even though the present collection contains a wide variety of texts and melodies, the reader will notice that only a comparatively few informants contributed to it. There is little doubt in my mind that were I to search farther among a greater number of people, I should find much material which would not duplicate the present songs. Wedding songs and immigrant songs are only partially represented. American factory and labor songs, lullabies and children's songs, as well as religious and historical ballads are missing altogether. When one considers the enormous wealth of folksongs known by the Polish folk, the 105 songs contributed by ten informants are but a small fraction of the whole. It is hoped, however, that this small number may indicate the rich musical background with which the Polish immigrant comes to the United States and to Detroit.

Because the variety of material which may be found in the category of folksong often challenges any attempt at strict classification, it is necessary to describe its character without limiting its scope. Bela Bartok aptly defines the folksong thus:

> The term "peasant music" connotes, broadly speaking, all the tunes which endure among the peasant class of any nation, in a more or less wide area and for a more or less long period, and constitutes a spontaneous expression of musical feeling of that class.—See Bela Bartok, *Hungarian Folk Music*, trans. M. D. Calovocoressi (London, 1931), p.l.

He states that the origin of a folksong is immaterial. The fact that it has been adopted by the peasant is sufficient proof of its present ownership and justifies its classification with musical art.

There are those who believe that folk music was created by individual minstrels or poets of a social group other than that of the peasant, and that folksongs gradually became diffused beyond the circle of their origin through the efforts of wandering minstrels. A study of some of the eighty-nine variants of "Jasio Konie Poił," No. 65, shows that the peasant can place upon a song so indelible a stamp of ownership that no one is justified in calling it an art song today. (See "An Analysis of the Polish Folk Songs," p. 217.) Other songs cannot claim such diversity; nevertheless, the folk have been singing them and so altering the text and music that they show characteristics of creative art. (See notes 3, 4, 34.)

The flexibility of the Polish language through the use of diminutives, which can be attached to nouns, adjectives and adverbs, has made it difficult to give the translation the exact shade of meaning which the Polish form possesses. The phrase, "the young oxen," in No. 50, does not possess the same connotation for the English reader that "wółki" does for the Polish reader or folksinger. To say "the dear oxen" or "the little oxen" is just as ineffectual. The Scotch terms "lassie," "bonnie" and the like are symbols which can give the English reader a clearer understanding of the effect which the diminutive has in Polish. In some cases, I have made no attempt to translate the diminutive into English, since nothing would be gained by it. Let it suffice to say that the diminutive is used extensively in Polish and that it gives the songs an illusive quality which defies translation.

The Polish text represents a wide range of Polish, from a given dialect to standard usage, with colloquial expressions in many of the songs. Because of the nature of the songs, I transcribed the recorded and dictated words as nearly like the spoken words as possible.

The translation of given names was difficult since only in some cases are the English equivalents satisfactory. However, for the sake of uniformity, I have used English equivalents throughout. For nonsense syllables, the translations use phonetic equivalents.

I have attempted metrical translation, however difficult, in order to preserve the rhythm and the coincidence of syllable and note of the original. The four-line stanza, usually in trochaic or dactyllic meter, with frequent spondees, is the most popular form in the present collection, with the six-line stanza next. In most songs, however, the latter form contains a repetition of third and fourth lines.

Repetition is a device which the Polish folksinger uses extensively. The patterns in repetition are as varied as are the songs. For instance, a four-line stanza can be extended to seven lines: 1, 2-3-4, 2-3-4, or 1, 2-2, 3-4, 3-4. A five-line stanza is extended to eleven lines: 1, 2-2, 3-3, 4-5-5, 4-5-5; and four lines are extended to ten: 1-2, 1-2, 3-3-4, 3-3-4. The variety of patterns is too numerous to describe at greater length, but it should be noted here that some singers never repeat a line, while others seldom sing a folksong without some pattern of repetition, thus incorporating repetition into their style as singers.

Aside from the repetition of lines, there are other patterns of interest used within the stanza, such as the incremental device (see Nos. 20, 89); the break in the middle of a line of thought with "a lu lu, a lu lu," a break which extends to the first part of the succeeding line, as in No. 68; and finishing each stanza on a similar thematic note although not with identical words, as in No. 44. Song No. 53 uses a clever inversion in lines three, four, and five of each stanza. In No. 51 the first stanza is repeated after stanzas 2, 3, 4, 5 and 6. In another song, the repeated stanza forms part of a dialog in a wedding song. (See No. 84.) Finally, the formal refrain is also used in a number of songs.

An interesting aspect of the Polish folk carol is the intimate relation between the peasant's daily life and the coming of the Christ Child, as in No. 79 for example. The event is described in dramatic dialog against a background of Polish shepherds and their many tribulations, all of which are telescoped in time and place into that first holy night in Bethlehem. Their joys are a combination of simple reverence and merry dance and song, executed to the music of fiddles and bagpipes. Their gifts come from their barnyards, fields, and woods. In contrast to No. 79, these carols are evidence not only of folk origin, but of the spontaneous creation of new stanzas. (See Nos. 80, 81, 82.)

The frequently recurring terms, "Mazur," "Kujawiak," and "Krakowiak," refer to the ethnographical divisions of ancient Poland. Today, they have little bearing upon the total picture of the country except in a retrospective or romantic view of the folk.

Contents

I

People sing because a mood moves them to do so.

Mood is a gentle persuader of boundless passion and satisfying power.

Sometimes it finds expression in the melody.

Sometimes it is an emotion like love, or joy, or pain, or pride, or longing.

I

Czekaj Tu Dziewczyno
WAIT FOR ME, MY DEAR GIRL

Sung in 1940 by Frank First, who learned it from his mother,
who had learned it in Sonina, Poland.

"Czekaj tu dziewczyno	"*Wait for me, my dear girl,*
W Utika na moście.	*On the Utica bridge.*
Czekaj tu dziewczyno	*Wait for me, my dear girl,*
W Utika na moście.	*On the Utica bridge.*
To ja ci na rybce,	*Then by way of a wee fish,*
To ja ci na rybce	*Then by way of a wee fish,*
Złote piórko poślę.	*A gold feather I'll send.*

To ja ci na rybce,
To ja ci na rybce
Złote piórko poślę."

"Nie jedna tu rybka
Bez ten mostek przeszła;
Jeszczem nie widziała,
Ani nie słyszała
Żeby piórko niosła.

Kopał tu studzienke,
Spoglądał też do niej.
"Żeby tak głęboka
Jaka jest szeroka,
Wskoczył-bym ja do niej."

A przy tej studzience,
Napojała pawia.
"Powiedz mi dziewczyno,
Powiedz mi jedyno,
Czy ty będziesz moja."

"Jakże ci ja powiem,
Skoro sama nie wiem?
Przyjedź do mnie w nocy,
Choćby o północy,
Od mamy się dowiem.

"Jak przyjedziesz do mnie,
Miej pare konisi.
Postaw je i przywiąż,
Postaw je i przywiąż,
U mojej jedlisi.

"Bo moja jedlisia
To jest ulubiona.
Jak w zimie tak w lecie,
Jak w lecie tak w zimie
Zawsze jest zielona."

Then by way of a wee fish,
Then by way of a wee fish,
A gold feather I'll send."

"More than one little fish
Swam beneath the bridge there,
Yet I ne'er have heard of,
Nor have I e'er seen, one
With a golden feather."

He was digging a well
And he measured its depth.
"If it were as deep as
It now measures in width,
I would leap into it."

And nearby the clear well,
She was tending peacocks.
"Tell me this, my dear girl,
Give me only one word.
Will you be my true love?"

"This I cannot answer
When myself I know not.
Come to me when night falls,
When 'tis well nigh midnight,
I'll have mother's counsel.

"When you ride up to me
With a pair of fine steeds,
Will you halt and tie them,
Will you halt and tie them,
To my dear green fir tree?

"For my little fir tree,
By me dearly treasured,
Be it winter, summer,
Be it summer, winter,
It does ever grow green."

2

Na Podolu Biały Kamień[1]

IN PODOLIA ON A WHITE ROCK

(See numbers 62 and 63)

Na Po - do - lu bia - ły ka - mień,
In Po - do - lia on a white rock,

Po - do - lan - ka sie - dzi na nim.
On a white rock, sits a maid - en.

Sie - dzi, sie - dzi, wie - niec wi - je,
There she sits and weaves a gar - land,

Z sa - mych róż i sa - mych li - lji.
Us - ing on - ly lil - ies, ros - es.

A ballad, sung in 1940 by Mrs. Helen Poplawska, who learned it in Lwow but could not recall all of it at the time of the recording.

Na Podolu biały kamień,	*In Podolia on a white rock,*
Podolanka siedzi na nim.	*On a white rock sits a maiden.*
Siedzi, siedzi, wieniec wije	*There she sits and weaves a garland,[2]*
Z samych róż i samych lilji.	*Using only lilies, roses.*

Przyszedł do niej cudzoziemiec.
"Podolanko, daj mi wieniec."
"Nie dam wieńca ani kwiata
Bo się boję mego brata."

"Ach otruj-że brata twego.
Będziesz miała mnie samego.
Idź do gaju zielonego;
Uchwyć węża zjadliwego.

"Posiekaj go na drobnego;
Ugotuj go na mięciutko.
. . . .
. . . ."

A brat pije; z konia leci.
"Siostro moja, dbaj o dzieci."
. . . .
. . . .

On this day there came a stranger.
"I would have your wreath, fair maiden."
"You'll have nought, not e'en a flower,
For I strongly fear my brother."

"Poison then your brother, I say.
You will have me for your true love.
Find a forest glade of green brush;
Trap a snake of deadly venom.

"Chop it well and mince it finely;
Boil it 'till it's soft and tender.
. . . .
. . . ."

Thus he drinks and from his horse falls.
"O my sister, love my children."
. . . .
. . . .

5

3
O Mój Rozmarynie, Rozwijaj Się
O MY ROSEMARY PLANT, BURST INTO BUD

Moderato

O mój roz - ma - ry - nie, roz - wi - jaj
O my rose - mar - y plant, burst in - to

się,
bud,
O mój roz - ma - ry - nie, roz - wi - jaj
O my rose - mar - y plant, burst in - to

się.
bud.
Pój-dę do dziew - czy - ny, Pój-dę do je -
I will go to my girl, I will see the

dy - nej, Za - py-tam się. Pój-dę do dziew - czy - ny,
one girl And woo her now. I will go to my girl,

pój - dę do je - dy - nej, Za - py - tam się.
I will see the one girl And woo her now.

Sung in 1940 by Mrs. Alexandra Szczepanik, who learned it from the Polish soldiers of World War I, who had stopped in Bircze on the way to the front.

6

O mój rozmarynie, rozwijaj się,	O my rosemary plant, burst into bud,
O mój rozmarynie, rozwijaj się.	O my rosemary plant, burst into bud.
Pójdę do dziewczyny,	I will go to my girl,
Pójdę do jedynej,	I will see the one girl
Zapytam się.	And woo her now.
Pójdę do dziewczyny,	I will go to my girl,
Pójdę do jedynej,	I will see the one girl
Zapytam się.	And woo her now.
A jak mi odpowie, "Nie kocham cię!"	And if she should answer, "I love you not,"
Ułani werbują,	Uhlans are recruiting,
Strzelcy maszerują	Sharpshooters are marching.
Zaciągnę się.	I will join them.
Dadzą mi konika cisawego,	They'll give me a roan horse, sure-footed, fleet,
I ostrą szabelkę,	And a sharp-edged sabre,
I ostrą szabelkę	And a sharp-edged sabre,
Do boku mego.	Fixed to my side.
Dadzą mi manierkę z gorzałczyną,	They'll give me a canteen, with vodka filled;
Ażebym nie tęsknił,	Then I'll not be yearning,
Ażebym nie tęsknił	Then I'll not be yearning
Za dziewczyną.	For any girl.

4
Zielona Ruta, Jałowiec[3]
GREEN GROW THE RUE AND JUNIPER

Con Grazia

"Zie - lo - na ru - ta, ja - ło -
"Green grow the rue and ju - ni -

wiec, Lep - szy mło - dzie - niec niż wdo -
per. Bet - ter a youth than wid - ow -

wiec. Zie - lo - na ru - ta drob - ny
er. Green grow the rue and ti - ny

kwiat. Wę - druj diew - czy - no ze mną w świat."
bud. Let's go forth, girl, in - to the world."

Sung in 1940 by Mrs. John Krupski, who learned it from friends
in Buffalo.

"Zielona ruta, jałowiec,   "Green grow the rue and juniper,
Lepszy młodzieniec niż wdowiec.   Better a youth than widower.
Zielona ruta, drobny kwiat,   Green grow the rue and tiny bud,
Wędruj dziewczyno ze mną w świat."   Let's go forth, girl, into the world."

8

"Jakże mam z tobą wędrować?
Będą się ludzie dziwować."
"A niech się ludzie dziwują.
Oboje młodzi wędrują.

"Zielona ruta, jałowiec,
Lepszy młodzieniec niż wdowiec.
Wdowiec będzie ci wymawiał
Że lepszą pierwszą żonkę miał.

"A dzieci będą płakały
Bodaj macochy nie znały.
I czeladź będzie mówiła
Lepiej nieboszczka rządziła.

"Zielona ruta, jałowiec,
Lepszy młodzieniec niż wdowiec.
Lepszy młodzieniec w kaftanie
Niżeli wdowiec w żupanie."

*"How can I wander off with you?
People will wonder at our act."
"O let the people be amazed.
We two young lovers will be off.*

*"Green grow the rue and juniper,
Better a youth than widower.
A widower will oft complain
That his first wife was far better.*

*"And oft his children too will rue
The day they met their stepmother.
Even the servants will declare
Their former mistress they prefer.*

*"Green grow the rue and juniper,
Better a youth than widower.
Better a youth in tunic poor
Than any well-dressed widower."*

5
Zakochałem-ci Się[4]
O IN LOVE I'VE FALLEN
(See number 43)

Za - ko - cha-łem-ci się Aż po sa - me u - szy;
O in love I've fall - en, Lock and stock and bar - rel;

Za - ko-cha-łem- ci się Aż po sa - me u - szy.
O in love I've fall - en, Lock and stock and bar - rel.

Rad bym Kaś - kę po - jąć, Rad bym z ca - łej du - szy;
Glad-ly would I wed Kate; All my heart's set on it;

Rad bym Kaś - kę po jąc, Rad bym z ca - łej du - szy.
Glad- ly would I wed Kate; All my heart's set on - it;

Raz, dwa, trzy, czte - ry! Raz, dwa, trzy!
One, two, three, four! And one, two, three!

Sung in 1940 by Mrs. Alexandra Szczepanik, who learned this song
from a village girl in Bircze, Poland.

Zakochałem-ci się   *O in love I've fallen,*
Aż po same uszy;   *Lock and stock and barrel;*

Zakochałem-ci się	*O in love I've fallen,*
Aż po same uszy.	*Lock and stock and barrel.*
Rad bym Kaśkę pojąć,	*Gladly would I wed Kate;*
Rad bym z całej duszy;	*All my heart's set on it.*
Rad bym Kaśkę pojąć,	*Gladly would I wed Kate;*
Rad bym z całej duszy.	*All my heart's set on it.*
Refren:	Refrain:
Raz, dwa, trzy, cztery!	*One, two, three, four!*
Raz, dwa, trzy!	*And one, two, three!*
Ale ta psiajucha,	*But alas! the vixen,*
Ta psiawiara Kaśka,	*That old meany, Katie,*
Co raz spojrzy na mnie,	*For each glance she gives me,*
To dziesięć na Jaśka.	*She gives ten to Johnny.*
Ale wiem co zrobię;	*Now I know what I'll do;*
Pójdę za wojaka;	*I'll become a soldier.*
Będę nosił szablę	*I will wear a fine sword*
Chodź półtora roka.	*Eighteen months without end.*
A jak mi się szczęście	*When the wheel of fortune*
Tam potoczy kołem,	*Turns its favors my way,*
To może zostanę	*Then perhaps I shall be*
Panem generałem.	*An exalted general.*
Jak pojadę przez wieś,	*When upon my grey horse*
Na siwem koniku,	*I ride through the village,*
Oj będzie tam będzie	*O there will be, will be*
Tych dziewuch bez liku.	*Many girls around me.*
Jak Kaśka zobaczy	*And when Katie sees me,*
Pana generała,	*An exalted general,*
Oj, będzie tam będzie	*Madly she will love me,*
Oj za mną szalała.	*Yes, O yes, that she will.*
A ja będę twardy,	*But I will be heartless,*
A potem to zmięknę	*Then I'll soften somewhat,*
I z moją Kasieńką	*And with my dear Katie*
Do ołtarza klęknę.	*At the altar I'll kneel.*
A Jaśka psiajuchę	*As for John, the villain,*
Wezmę za pastucha.	*He will be my swineherd.*
Niech się memu szczęściu	*Let him be a witness*
Napatrzy, nasłucha.	*To my wondrous fortune.*
A jak nas Pan Jezus	*And when our Lord Jesus*
Opatrzy dziatkami,	*Blesses us with children,*
Będą takie piękne	*They will be as handsome*
Jako i my sami.	*E'en as we ourselves are.*

6

Umarł Maciek, Umarł[5]

MAT IS DEAD, ALAS, DEAD!

U - marł Ma - ciek, u - marł. Już le - ży na
Mat   is dead,   a - las   dead, He's   laid out   in

des - ce.   Że - by mu   za - gra - li,
his   shroud.   Let   the   mu - sic   ring   out.

Pod - sko - czył   by   jesz - cze.   Oj szko - da   go,
He'll   dance for   us   a - gain.   What   a   pit - y,

Bo - że wiecz - ny,   Bo z Mać - ka był   Czło - wiek grze - czny.
Lord   Al - might - y.   Mat   was sure - ly.   Al - ways jol - ly.

Oj   da - na da - na   Da - na   da - na   da - na!
O   da - na da - na   Da - na   da - na   da - na!

Sung in 1945 by Frank First, who did not remember where he had
learned this popular folksong.

Umarł Maciek, umarł.
Już leży na desce.
Żeby mu zagrali,
Podskoczył by jeszcze.
Oj szkoda go,
Boże wieczny,
Bo z Maćka był
Człowiek grzeczny.
Oj dana dana
Dana dana dana!

Mat is dead, alas, dead!
He's laid out in his shroud.
Let the music ring out.
He'll dance for us again.
What a pity,
Lord Almighty.
Mat was surely
Always jolly.
O dana dana
Dana dana dana!

7

Przeleciał-ci Słowiczek, Słowiczek

YONDER FLEW A NIGHTINGALE, NIGHTINGALE

Allegretto

Prze - le - ciał - ci   sło - wi - czek,
Yon - der   flew   a   night - in - gale,

sło - wi - czek,   Przez zie - lo - ny   ga - i - czek,
night - in - gale,   Through the glade of   green, green trees,

Przez ga - i - czek,   przez zie - lo - ny,
Through the glade,   the   ev - er green   glade,

Do dziew - czy - ny   u - lu - bio - nej.
To   the   girl   that   I   love dear - ly.

Sung in 1941 by Frank First, who learned it from his mother.
She had learned it in Sonina, Poland.

Przeleciał-ci słowiczek, słowiczek,	*Yonder flew a nightingale, nightingale,*
Przez zielony gaiczek,	*Through the glade of green green trees,*
Przez gaiczek, przez zielony,	*Through the glade, the ever green glade,*
Do dziewczyny ulubionej.	*To the girl that I love dearly.*
Przez gaiczek, przez zielony,	*Through the glade, the ever green glade,*
Do dziewczyny ulubionej.	*To the girl that I love dearly.*

Jasio siadł na konisia, konisia;
Upadła mu szablisia.
"Chodź mi Maryś szable podaj,
Tylko do mnie nic nie gadaj."

Marysia mu podała, podała,
I rzewnie zapłakała.
"Ty pojedziesz, ja zostanę.
A kogoż ja będę miała?

"Kiedy mnie ty tak kochasz, tak kochasz,
To posprzedaj co tam masz.
To posprzedaj pola, łąki,
A mnie wykup z tej wojenki."

"Pola, łąki nie sprzedam, nie sprzedam,
Bo ja z łąki korzyść mam.
Bo ja z łąki siano koszę,
Ciebie Jasiu w sercu noszę."

"Kiedy mnie ty tak kochasz, tak kochasz,
To posprzedaj co tam masz.
To posprzedaj kamienice,
A mnie wykup z tej konnicy."

"Kamienicy nie sprzedam, nie
Z kamienicy ładny dom.   [sprzedam.
W kamienicy będę mieszkać."
Ciebie Jasiu będę kochać."

"Kiedy mnie ty tak kochasz, tak kochasz,
To posprzedaj co tam masz.
To posprzedaj krowy, woły,
A mnie wykup z tej niewoli."

Krowy, woły sprzedała, sprzedała,
I Jasieńka dostała.
Krowy, woły posprzedała,
A ciebie Jasiu dostała.

Johnny sat astride his horse, 'stride his horse:
His sword fell down to the ground.
"Mary dear, come hand it to me;
Please say naught to me, I beg you."

Mary handed him the sword, him the sword,
Weeping softly, woefully,
"You are leaving me, my darling;
O who will console my heart now?"

"If you really love me so, love me so,
Sell all things that you possess.
Sell your fields and all your pastures;
Buy me out of battle service."

"Fields and pastures I'll ne'er sell, I'll ne'er
For my fields provide my bread.   [sell,
In the fields I harvest the hay;
In my heart I'll keep you alway."

"If you really love me so, love me so,
Sell all things that you possess.
Sell your mansion built of stone;
Buy me out of cavalry service."

"My stone mansion I'll not sell, I'll not sell;
It makes a fair home for me.
I will live in this fair mansion;
I will keep you safe in my heart."

"If you really love me so, love me so,
Sell all things that you possess.
Sell your oxen, sell your cows;
Buy my freedom from this bondage."

Cows and oxen Mary sold, Mary sold,
And she got her beloved John.
She sold all her cows and oxen
Just to have you, Johnny dear.

8

*Choćbym Ja Jeździł We Dnie I W Nocy*⁶
THOUGH I SHOULD TRAVEL ALL DAY AND ALL NIGHT

(See number 9)

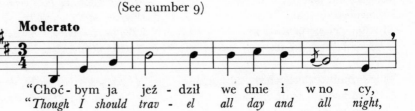

"Choć-bym ja jeż - dził we dnie i w no - cy,
"Though I should trav - el all day and all night,

Choć - bym wy - jeż dził ko - nio - wi o - czy,
Though I should ride my poor horse un - to death,

Prze - cież ty mu - sisz mo - ją być, Mo - ją
You should know you must be mine, dear, And my

wo - lę wy - peł - nić. Prze-cież ty mu - sisz
will you must ful - fill. You should know you must

mo - ją być, Mo - ją wo - lę wy - peł - nić."
be mine, dear, And my will you must ful - fill."

Sung in 1941 by Frank First, who learned it at a Detroit picnic
from an unknown singer.

"Choćbym ja jeździł we dnie i w nocy,
Choćbym wyjeździł koniowi oczy,
Przecież ty musisz moją być,
Moją wolę wypełnić.
Przecież ty musisz moją być,
Moją wolę wypełnić."

"A ja się stanę drobną ptaszyną
Będę latała gęstą krzewiną.
Przecież ja nie chcę twoją być,
Twoją wolę wypełnić."

"Mają tu cieśle takie przybory
Co wycinają lasy i bory.
Przecież itd."

"A ja się stanę małą rybeczką
Będę pływała bystrą wodeczką.
Przecież itd."

"Mają rybacy takie siateczki
Co wyłapują małe rybeczki.
Przecież itd."

"A ja się stanę dzikiem kaczorem,
Będę pływała wielkiem jeziorem.
Przecież itd."

"Mają tu strzelcy takowe strzelby
Co wypalają kaczorom we łby.
Przecież itd."

"A ja się stanę gwiazdą na niebie,
Będę świeciła ludziom w potrzebie.
Przecież itd."

"A ja mam litość nad ubogiemi,
Sproszę ja gwiazdy z nieba ku ziemi.
Przecież itd."

"Już teraz widzę Boskie zarządy,
Gdzie się obróce, znajdziesz mnie
Już teraz muszę twoją być, [wszędzie.
Wolę twoją wypełnić."

"*Though I should travel all day and all night,*
Though I should ride my poor horse unto death,
You should know you must be mine, dear,
And my will you must fulfill.
You should know you must be mine, dear,
And my will you must fulfill."

"*I shall become a bird of the air,*
Flying about the thicket and woodland.
Thus you see I will not be yours,
And your will I'll not fulfill."

"*Carpenters have such powerful tools,*
Forests and woods can be felled at will.
You should etc."

"*I shall become a fish of the sea*
And swim in yon rapid waters.
Thus you etc."

"*Fishermen's nets are of such fine measure,*
The smallest fish can be snared by them.
You should etc."

"*I shall become a drake of the wilds;*
I shall swim over wide open lakes.
Thus you etc."

"*But hunters' guns can reach out so far,*
Even wild drakes are shot through the head.
You should etc."

"*I shall become a star of the heavens,*
And I shall shine on people in need.
Thus you etc."

"*I have compassion on needy people;*
I shall strew all the stars at their feet.
You should etc."

"*Now I can see that this is God's plan;*
Where'er I turn, there find me you will.
I know at last I must be yours,
All your wishes to fulfill."

9
Choćbym Ja Jeździł We Dnie I W Nocy
THOUGH I SHOULD TRAVEL ALL DAY AND ALL NIGHT

(Variant of number 8 in music)

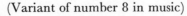

Allegretto

"Choć - bym ja jeź-dził we dnie i w no - cy,
"Though   I should trav - el   all   day and all night,

Choć - bym wy jeź - dził ko - nio - wi o - czy,
Though   I should ride my poor   horse un - to death,

Prze - cież   ty mu - sisz   mo - ją
You   should   know   you   must   be   mine,

być,   Mo - ją   wo - lę   wy - peł - nić!"
dear,   And my   will   you   must ful - fill."

Sung in 1941 by Mrs. John Krupski, who learned it from her
mother in Buffalo. The Polish text is the same as in number 8, but since
the music is different, the English translation must be
different to fit the music.

"Though I should travel all day and all night,
Though I should ride my poor horse unto death,
You should know you must be mine, dear,
And my will you must fulfill."

"I shall become a wee bird of the air,
Flying about the thicket and woodland.
You see I will never be yours,
And your will I'll not fulfill."

"Woodmen have tools of such power and size,
Forests and woods can be felled at their will.
You should know etc."

"I shall become a wee fish of the sea,
I'll swim about in yon rapid waters.
You see I will never etc."

"Fishermen have nets of such fine measure,
E'en the smallest fish can be snared by them.
You should know etc."

"I shall become a strong drake of the wilds,
I shall swim over wild, dangerous lakes.
You see I will never etc."

"Hunters have guns that can reach out so far,
Even wild drakes can be shot through the head.
You should know etc."

"Then I'll become a star in the heavens
And I shall shine on the humble and poor.
You see I will never etc."

"I have compassion on people in need;
I shall strew all the stars at their poor feet.
You should know etc."

"Now I can see that all this is God's plan.
Where'er I shall turn, there find me you will.
Now I know I must be yours, dear,
All your wishes to fulfill."

10

Śliczne Gwoździki[7]

LOVELY CARNATIONS

(See number 11)

Moderato - legato

Ślicz - ne gwoź dzi - ki, Pięk-ne tu - li - pa - ny.
Love - ly car - na - tions, Charm-ing, grace - ful tu - lips.

Gdzie żeś, ach gdzie - żeś Sta-siu mój ko - cha -ny?
Where is, O where is Stan-ley, my be - lov - ed,

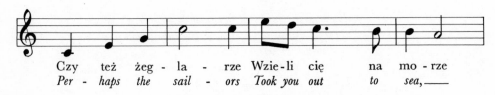

Czy też żeg - la - rze Wzie-li cię na mo - rze
Per - haps the sail - ors Took you out to sea,___

Że się me ser - ce U - tu - lić nie mo - że?
For my poor heart___ can - not be con-sol - ed.

Sung in 1941 by Mrs. John Krupski, who had learned it in her youth
from friends in Buffalo.

Śliczne gwoździki,	*Lovely carnations,*
Piękne tulipany.	*Charming graceful tulips.*
Gdzie-żeś, ah gdzie-żeś	*Where is, O where is*
Stasiu mój kochany?	*Stanley, my beloved?*
Czy też żeglarze	*Perhaps the sailors*
Wzięli cię na morze	*Took you out to sea,*
Że się me serce	*For my poor heart*
Utulić nie moźe?	*Cannot be consolèd.*

20

Astrologowie
Co gwiazdy liczycie,
Czy wy o mojem
Stasieczku nie wiecie?
Może wpadł w niemoc
Może biedę znosi,
Może zapomniał
O swej lubej Zosi.

O serce, serce,
Cóż mi za radę dasz?
Kogom kochała
Nie masz go już niemasz.
Oj! niemasz, niemasz
I może nie będzie.
Któż mnie sierotę
Rozweselać będzie?

And you astrologers,
You who count the stars,
What can you tell me
About my dear Stanley?
Does he lie stricken?
Does he suffer dire need?
Has he forgotten
His belovèd Sophie?

O heart, do tell me
How to be consolèd.
The one I have loved
I do not have near me.
Do not have near me,
And perhaps may never.
Who then will comfort
This poor grieving orphan?

11

Śliczne Gwoździki

LOVELY CARNATIONS

(Variant of number 10)

Andante-legato

"Ślicz - ne, gwoź dzi - ki, Pięk-ne
"Love - ly car - na - tions, Charm-ing,

tu - li - pa - ny. Gdzie - żeś ach gdzie -
grace - ful tu - lips. Where is, O where

żeś Sta - siu mój ko - cha - ny? Gdzie -
is Stan-ley, my be - lov - ed? Where

żeś, ach gdzie - żeś Sta - siu mój ko-cha - ny.
is, O where is Stan-ley my be - lov - ed.

Sung in 1941 by Frank First, who learned it while singing with a
Polish choral society in Detroit.

"Sliczne gwoździki,
Piękne tulipany.
Gdzie-żeś, ach gdzie-żeś
Stasiu mój kochany?
Gdzie-żeś, ach gdzie-żeś
Stasiu mój kochany?

"*Lovely carnations,*
Charming graceful tulips.
Where is, O where is
Stanley, my beloved?
Where is, O where is
Stanley, my beloved?

"Czy cię na wojnie
Kula zła trafiła,
Że próżno czeka
Twa dziewczyna miła?"

"Nie smuć się dziewcze,
Nie lej łez aniele.
Przyjedzie Stasiu,
Wyprawi wesele.

"Huczne wesele
Z muzyką na przedzie,
I do ołtarza
Dumnie cię powiedzie.

"Zagrają skrzypki,
I zadudnią basy;
Zabrzmią mazury,
Chuczne obertasy.

"I w taniec ruszy
Calutka gromada.
A matuś twoja
Będzie patrzeć rada.

"A kiedy wreszcie
Już ustaną tany,
Zostanie jeno
Stasio twój kochany.

"I będzie kochał,
Kochał bez przestanku,
W dzień do wieczora
Z wieczora do ranka."

"*Perhaps in battle
A stray bullet found you,
And your beloved
Yearns thus vainly for you.*"

"*Grieve not, my dear girl,
Do not weep, my angel.
Stanley will come back,
And there'll be a wedding.*

"*A gala wedding
With gay music all day;
Proudly he'll take you
To the marriage altar.*

"*Fiddlers will strike up,
Bass violas will groan,
Mazurs will ring out,
Obereks will thunder.*

"*And everybody
Will be dancing, swirling.
Your mother proudly
Will behold the triumph.*

"*And finally when
All the dancing will cease,
You will be left with
Your belovèd Stanley.*

"*And he will love you,
Love you without end,
From dawn till ev'ning,
From ev'ning until dawn.*"

12

Na Środku Pola

IN THE MEADOWLAND

Andante cantabile

"Na środ - ku po - la _____
"In the mead - ow - land _____

Roś - nie to - po - la. _____ Po - wiedz-
Grows a pop - lar tree. _____ Tell me

że mi, mo - ja mi - ła, Czy bę -
true, my lit - tle dar - ling, Will you

1. dziesz mo - ja?" _____ **6.** gu - mi - na."_____
be my love?"_____ for our guests."_____

Sung in 1941 by Frank First, who learned it from his mother,
who had learned it in Sonina, Poland.

Na środku pola
Rośnie topola.
Powiedz-że mi, moja miła,
Czy będziesz moja.
Powiedz-że mi, moja miła,
Czy będziesz moja."

"In the meadowland
Grows a poplar tree.
Tell me true, my little darling,
Will you be my love?
Tell me true, my little darling,
Will you be my love?"

"Jak ja będę twoja,
To ci rączkę dam,
I ten wianek z rozmarynu
Co w ogródku mam.

"Dam ja ci go dam,
Mój najmilejszy.
Położe-ci na ołtarzu
W kościele na Mszy."

"Tam będą nam grać
I ładnie śpiewać,
A my młodzi zasmuceni
Będziemy ślub brać.

"Nasze dróżeczki
Wezmą chusteczki
I ocierać będą młodej
Spłakane oczki.

"Przyjdziem z kościoła;
Będzie gościna;
Chleb z maselkiem, miód z kukiełką
I legumina."

*"When you win my love,
You will have my hand
And a garland of rosemary
From my garden fair.*

*"I shall offer it
To you, my dear love.
I shall place it on the altar
At the wedding Mass."*

*"Musicians will play
And the choir will sing,
And we saddened, youthful lovers
Will speak our vows then.*

*"And all our bridesmaids
Will have handkerchiefs
And they will be drying the eyes
Of the weeping bride.*

*"We shall leave the church.
There will be a feast;
Bread and butter, rolls and honey,
Pastries for our guests."*

13

Chodziłem Po Polu

THROUGH THE FIELDS I WANDER

Moderato

Cho - dzi - łem po po - lu I zbie - ra - łem kło - sy.
Through the fields I wan - der, Gath-er - ing my har - vest.

Ko-cham tą dziew - czy - nę Co ma zło - te wło - sy,
I love the girl dear - ly With the gold - en tress - es,

Co ma zło - te wło - sy I o - czy nie - bie - skie.
With the gold - en tress - es. And the eyes of deep blue.

Na-wet bym ją nie - dał Za ber - ło kró - lew - skie.
Nev- er would I trade her for a roy - al scep - tre.

Sung in 1940 by Mrs. Sophia Dziob, who learned it from friends in
Passaic, New Jersey.

Chodziłem po polu	*Through the fields I wander,*
I zbierałem kłosy.	*Gathering my harvest.*
Kocham tą dziewczynę	*I love the girl dearly*
Co ma złote włosy,	*With the golden tresses,*
Co ma złote włosy	*With the golden tresses*
I oczy niebieskie.	*And the eyes of deep blue.*
Nawet bym ją nie dał	*Never would I trade her*
Za berło królewskie.	*For a royal sceptre.*

Bo berło królewskie
Nie ma tej słodyczy,
A dziewczyna czasem
Buziaka użyczy,
Buziaka użyczy,
Przyciśnie do siebie.
Wtedy człowiekowi
Tak miło jak w niebie.

For a royal sceptre
Lacks that certain sweetness,
But a girl will sometimes
Volunteer a sweet kiss,
Volunteer a sweet kiss,
Press you closely to her.
It is then a man knows
Heaven smiles upon him.

14

Przywiozę Z Miasteczka

I SHALL BUY YOU RIBBONS

Sung in 1941 by Mrs. Sophia Dziob, who learned it from her husband,
who had learned it in Nowy Sącz, Poland.

Przywiozę z miasteczka	*I shall buy you ribbons*
Wstążek pięknych zwój,	*When I go to town,*
Boś ładna dziewczynka	*For you are my beauty*
A ja chłopiec twój.	*And I am your love.*
Przy tobie usiądę	*I'll sit down beside you*
W oczki patrzę twe	*And look in your eyes.*
I kochać cię będę	*I'll love you forever*
Boś kochanie me.	*For you are my love.*

Wstążki krasne, piękne!
Ładną buzie masz!
Całusa ukradnę
Jeśli mi nie dasz.
Przy tobie usiądę
W oczki patrzę twe
I kochać cię będę
Boś kochanie me.

Rainbow colored ribbons!
Lips so beautiful!
A kiss from you I'll steal
Unless you give one.
I'll sit down beside you
And look in your eyes.
I'll love you forever,
For you are my love.

15

Pójdę Do Sadu

WITHIN MY GARDEN

Moderato

Pój - dę do sa - du, Na - zry wam róż,
With - in my gar - den, Ros - es I'll pluck.

I zwi - ję wia - nek. Roz - myś - lam wciąż
Weav - ing a gar - land, I pon - der thus:

Że - by mi Pan Bóg Ta - kie - go dał
Lord, be it Thy will To grant me one

Co by ma - ją - tek, U - ro - dę miał.
Who will be wealth - y And hand - some too.

Sung in 1941 by Mrs. John Krupski, who learned it from her sister
in Buffalo.

Pójdę do sadu,	*Within my garden,*
Nazrywam róż,	*Roses I'll pluck.*
I zwiję wianek.	*Weaving a garland,*
Rozmyślam wciąż	*I ponder thus:*
Żeby mi Pan Bóg	*Lord, be it Thy will*
Takiego dał	*To grant me one*
Co by majątek,	*Who will be wealthy*
Urodę miał.	*And handsome too.*

Żeby był dobry
I kochał mnie.
Tego ja pragnę
A więcej nie.
Żeby był dobry
I kochał mnie,
Tego ja pragnę
A więcej nie.

May he be kindly,
Loving me true.
For this my heart yearns
And nothing more.
May he be kindly,
Loving me true.
For this my heart yearns
And nothing more.

16

Którędy Jasiu Pojedziesz

JOHNNY, WHICHEVER ROAD YOU TAKE

Con grazia

Któ-rę - dy Ja - siu po - je-dziesz, Ja - ka ci dro - ga
John - ny, which-ev - er road you take, Which ev - er road you

wy - pad-nie, Czy la - sy, gór - ry, do - li - ny,
trav - el by, Be it through woods o'er hills or dales,

Czy wo - da wa - bi cię zdrad-nie.___ Czy la - sy, gó - ry,
Wa - ters and all will treach'- rous be.___ Be it through woods o'er

do - li - ny, Czy wo - da wa - bi cię zdrad-nie.
hills or dales, Wa - ters and all will treach'- rous be.

Sung in 1941 by Frank First, who learned it while singing with a
Polish choral society.

Którędy Jasiu pojedziesz,	*Johnny, whichever road you take,*
Jaka ci droga wypadnie,	*Whichever road you travel by,*
Czy lasy, góry, doliny,	*Be it through woods, o'er hills or dales,*
Czy woda wabi cię zdradnie.	*Waters and all will treach'rous be.*
Czy lasy, góry, doliny,	*Be it through woods, o'er hills or dales,*
Czy woda wabi cię zdradnie.	*Waters and all will treach'rous be.*

Oj nie jedź Jasiu przez lasy,
Bo tam źli siedzą zbójowie.
Zabiją ciebie, Jasieńku.
Co na to matka twa powie?

Oj nie jedź Jasiu przez góry,
Bo tam w przepaściach stracisz ślad.
Spadniesz w głębokie wąwozy.
Już cię nie ujrzy więcej świat.

Oj nie jedź Jasiu w dolinę;
Tam czarownica czycha zła.
Upoi ciebie omami;
Zapomniesz że cię kocham ja.

Oj nie jedź Jasiu przez wodę;
Nie wierz szumowi modrych fal.
Porwie cię woda, zabierze,
Uniesie już na zawsze w dal.

Zostań Jasieńku; nie jedź, nie.
Czy źle ci ze mną, jedyny?
Bo jak pojedziesz, Jasieńku,
Zapomniesz swojej dziewczyny.

Johnny, do not ride through the woods,
You will find evil outlaws there.
They will kill you, my dearest John.
What will your mother say to that?

Johnny, do not ride o'er the hills;
You will be lost in deep ravines.
You may plunge into some abyss;
Never again will we see you.

Johnny, do not ride through the dales;
There awaits you an evil witch.
Wicked spells she will cast o'er you;
You will forget that I love you.

Johnny, do not sail o'er the sea.
Trust not the blue waves' siren call.
Rivers can seize and bear you off;
Forever lost to us you'll be.

Johnny, do stay; do not go forth.
Are you unhappy here, my love?
If you do leave, my dearest John,
You'll soon forget about your girl.

17

Hej! Od Krakowa Jadę

HEY! I AM LEAVING KRAKOW

Allegretto

Hej! od Kra - ko - wa ja - dę W da -
Hey! I am leav - ing Kra - kow For

le kie ob - ce stro - ny, Bo mi nie chcie - li dać
strange and dis - tant plac - es. They would not let me have

Ho sa dy - na! Ma - ry - si u - lu - bio - nej.
Ho sa dy - na! my dear be - lov - èd Ma - ry.

Bo mi nie chcie - li dać Ho sa dy - na!
They would not let me have Ho sa dy - na!

Ma - ry - si u - lu - bio - nej.
my dear be - lov - èd Ma - ry.

Sung in 1940 by Mrs. Alexandra Szczepanik, who learned it in Poland
from a peasant girl, who was herding cows near Bircze.

Hey! od Krakowa jadę
W dalekie obce strony,
Bo mi nie chcieli dać
Ho sa dyna! Marysi ulubionej.
Bo mi nie chcieli dać
Ho sa dyna! Marysi ulubionej.

Hey! szerokiem gościncem
Jedzie wóz za wozem.
Jak mi cię nie dadzą
Maryś moja, to przebiję się nożem.

Hey! przebiję się nożem,
Lub utopię się w Wiśle.
Żebyś ty wiedziała, Maryś moja,
Jak ja o tobie myślę.

Oj jak bym ja cię ściskał,
Jak bym ja całował
Ten buziak czerwony jak maliny,
Oj ten by mi smakował.

I chociaż nie będziemy
Mieli wielkiego wiana,
Oj będziem się kochać
Maryś moja, od wieczora do rana.

Hey! I am leaving Krakow
For strange and distant places.
They would not let me have—
Ho sa dyna! my dear belovèd Mary.
They would not let me have—
Ho sa dyna! my dear belovèd Mary.

Hey! Wagon after wagon
Rolls over the wide highway.
I will pierce my heart if
They will not let me have you, dearest Mary.

Hey! I will pierce my heart
Or drown in the Vistula.
If only you could know
How I long for you, Mary, my belovèd.

O how I would embrace you,
And how I would kiss those lips
Red as ripened berries.
Ho sa dyna! How I yearn for their sweet taste.

And though never shall we have
A great fortune when we wed,
We shall love each other
From early eve, dear Mary, till break of dawn.

18

Kalina, Kalina[8]

GUELDER ROSE, MY GUELDER

Moderato

"Ka - li - na, ka - li - na, Ró - ża far - bo - wa - na.
"Guel - der rose, my guel - der, Paint - ed blos - som thou art.

Po - wia - da - ją chłop - cy Żem ja ma - lo - wa - na.
All the boys are say - ing I am paint - ed al - so.

Ni ja ma - lo - wa - na, Ni ja far - bo - wa - na,
I have not been paint - ed, Nor have I been tint - ed.

Tyl - ko od ro - dzi - ców Pięk - nie wy - cho - wa - na."
I've been reared with pa - tience By my lov - ing par - ents."

Sung in 1941 by Mrs. John Krupski, who learned it from her mother
in Buffalo.

"Kalina, kalina,
Róża farbowana.
Powiadają chłopcy
Żem ja malowana.
Ni ja malowana,
Ni ja farbowana,
Tylko od rodziców
Pięknie wychowana.

"Guelder rose, my guelder,
Painted blossom thou art.
All the boys are saying
I am painted also.
I have not been painted,
Nor have I been tinted.
I've been reared with patience
By my loving parents.

36

"Trzewiczek się podarł,
Podeszewka cała.
Nie siadaj koło mnie
Bo ja jeszcze mała.
Nie siadaj koło mnie,
Nie zalecaj mi się.
Nie mam mająteczka,
Nie spodobam ci się."

"A żebyś ty była
Uboga sierota,
Nie miała byś wianka
Ze szczerego złota.
Tylko byś ty miała
Z tej pięknej kaliny
Co by ci uwiły
Te piękne dziewczyny.

"A tyś powiedziała
Zem ci wianek ukradł.
Wodeś nabierała;
W studzienkę ci upadł.
Sięgaj go, sięgaj
Prawą rączką do dna.
Jeśli go dosięgniesz,
Będziesz wianka godna."

"Sięgam go, sięgam,
Ale już nie cały.
Cztery perły złota
Z niego obleciały.
Sięgam go, sięgam,
Ale już nie cały.
Cztery perły złota
Z niego obleciały."

"*Lo, my shoe is damaged
Though the sole's like new yet.
Do not sit so near me,
I'm too young for wooing.
Do not sit so near me,
Do not look at me thus.
Wealth and fortune I've none;
That would never please you.*"

"*Were it true that you were
Poor, an orphaned creature,
You wouldn't have a garland
Woven of pure gold, dear.
But these pretty maidens
Would have woven for you
Dainty guelder roses.
Such would be your garland.*

"*Ah now, you are saying
I have stolen your garland.
You were drawing water;
It dropped in the well, dear.
Reach for it, my dear girl,
Daintily with your right hand.
Should you reach down deeply,
You will be rewarded.*"

"*I have reached it, reached it,
But alas! 'Tis broken.
Four wee pearls of pure gold
Will be ever missing.
I have reached it, reached it,
But alas! 'Tis broken.
Four wee pearls of pure gold
Will be ever missing.*"

19

Czterym Latka⁹

FOUR YEARS HAVE I

Con brio

Czte - rym lat - ka Wier - nie słu - żył,
Four   years have   I   Been   most   faith - ful,

Wier - nie słu - żył Gos - po - da - rzo - wi,
Been   most   faith - ful   To   my   mas - ter's   will,

Gos - po - da - rzo - wi.   Ra - nom wsta - wał,
To   my   mas - ter's   will.   I   rose   ear - ly

Siecz-kiem kra - jał   In - wen - ta - rzo - wi, da da - na. Ra-
Chaff   to   cut___   For the   hun - gry   herd, da   da - na.   I

nom wsta - wał, Siecz - kiem kra - jał   In - wen - ta - rzo - wi.
rose   ear - ly   Chaff   to   cut___   For the   hun - gry   herd.

Sung in 1941 by Mrs. John Krupski, who learned it from her mother
in Buffalo.

Czterym latka	*Four years have I*
Wiernie służył,	*Been most faithful,*
Wiernie służył	*Been most faithful*
Gospodarzowi,	*To my master's will,*
Gospodarzowi.	*To my master's will.*
Ranom wstawał,	*I rose early*
Sieczkiem krajał	*Chaff to cut*
Inwentarzowi, da dana.	*For the hungry herd, da dana.*
Ranom wstawał,	*I rose early*
Sieczkiem krajał	*Chaff to cut*
Inwentarzowi.	*For the hungry herd.*
A to wszystko	*All this I did*
Dla dziewczęcia,	*For the girl's sake*
Miło mi było,	*And happy I was,*
Bo mi serce	*For my poor heart,*
Jak żywica	*Just like resin,*
Do niej przylgnęło, da dana.	*Closely clung to her, da dana.*
Nie śmiałem się	*I dared not to*
Jej zapytać	*Ask this fair girl*
Czyby mnie chciała.	*If she would be mine.*
Bo dwa wółki	*Oxen she had,*
I dwie krówki	*And two heifers*
W posagu miała, da dana.	*As her dowry right, da dana.*
Miała ona	*In addition*
I co więcej,	*She had also*
I pierścień złoty.	*Rings of purest gold,*
I fartuszek	*And an apron*
Srebrem tkany,	*Loomed in silver*
Cudnej roboty, da dana.	*Crafted wondrously, da dana.*
Ale mi się	*One day it was*
Nadarzyła	*My good fortune*
Dziewczęcia zguba.	*To see her downfall.*
Kiedym sobie	*It was while I*
Wółki pasał,	*Grazed the oxen,*
Przy mnie i Kuba, da dana.	*Fido was with me, da dana.*
Przyleciała	*She came running,*
Zadyszana,	*Breathing deeply,*
"Ach ratuj! Stasiu!	*"Stanley, do help me!*
Wilk mi owce	*Sheep are scattered*
Porozganiał!	*By a bad wolf.*
Umrę ze strachu, da dana.	*I shall die of fright, da dana."*

20

Od Listka Do Listka

FROM LEAFLET TO LEAFLET

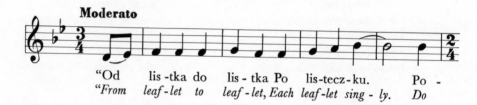

"Od lis-tka do lis-tka Po lis-tecz-ku. Po-
"From leaf-let to leaf-let, Each leaf-let sing-ly. Do

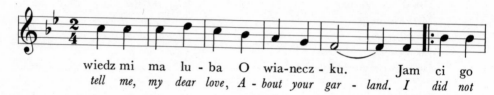

wiedz mi ma lu-ba O wia-necz-ku. Jam ci go
tell me, my dear love, A-bout your gar-land. I did not

nie wziął, A-ni nie u-kradł, Tyl-ko ci
take it, Nor did I steal it. Your gar-land,

ma lu-ba, Do wo-dy u-padł. Jam u-padł."
my dear love, Fell in the wa-ter. I wa-ter."

Sung in 1941 by Frank First, who learned it while singing with a
Polish choir group in Detroit.

"Od listka do listka
Po listeczku.
Powiedz mi ma luba
O wianeczku.
Jam ci go nie wziął,
Ani nie ukradł,
Tylko ci ma luba,
Do wody upadł.

"From leaflet to leaflet,
Each leaflet singly.
Do tell me, my dear love,
About your garland.
I did not take it,
Nor did I steal it.
Your garland, my dear love,
Fell in the water.

Jam ci go nie wziął,
Ani nie ukradł,
Tylko ci ma luba,
Do wody upadł."

"Od słowa do słowa,
Po słóweczku.
Nie rób mi wyrzutów,
Kochaneczku.
Byłam ci wierna,
Przy tobie stałam,
I ciebie jednego
W życiu kochałam."

"Od chatki do chatki,
Do chateczki.
Nie miałem ja innej
Kochaneczki.
Tyś była jedna,
Jedna jedyna.
Tyś najkochańsza
Moja dziewczyna."

"Od wioski do wioski
Do wioseczki.
Wędrują ludowe
Pioseneczki.
Już całe wieki
W podróży były,
Nim do nas z za morza
Z dala przybyły."

I did not take it,
Nor did I steal it.
Your garland, my dear love,
Fell in the water."

"From one word to another
Each trivial word.
Do not cast reproaches.
My belovèd.
I have been faithful,
True to you always,
And you're the only man
I have so lovèd."

"From cottage to cottage
To the smallest one.
No sweetheart have I had
Other than you.
You've been my only,
My one and only;
You are my belovèd,
My only loved one."

"From village to village,
To tiny hamlet.
The songs of our people
Have wandered for years.
For centuries now
They have been trav'ling
Ere they have come to us
From o'er the great sea."

21

Leciały Gęsie[10]

GEESE FLYING HIGH

Moderato

Le - cia-ły gę - sie Z Pol - ski do Ru - si,
Geese fly-ing high from Po - land to Rus - sia,

Z Pol - ski do Ru - si. Zmą - ci-ły wo -
Po - land to Rus - sia. They mud-died the

den - kę Na - dob-nej Zo - si, Zmą - ci - ły
wa - ter For pret - ty So - phie. They mud - died

wo - den - kę Na - dob - nej Zo - si.
the wa - ter for pret - ty So - phie.

Sung in 1940 by Mrs. Sophia Dziob, who learned it from a friend
in Tomaszowce, Poland.

Leciały gęsie
Z Polski do Rusi,
Z Polski do Rusi.
Zmąciły wodenkę
Nadobnej Zosi,
Zmąciły wodenkę
Nadobnej Zosi.

Geese flying high from
Poland to Russia,
Poland to Russia.
They muddied the water
For pretty Sophie.
They muddied the water
For pretty Sophie.

Jak jej zmąciły
Tak się ustała.
Nadobna Zosieńka
Chusteczki prała.

Chusteczki prała;
Jasio konie poił.
"Ej my-se, Zosieńko,
My-se oboje.

"My-se oboje;
My-se jednej myśli.
Pójdziemy do sadu;
Narwiemy wiśni.

"Narwiemy wiśni;
Narwiemy i gruszek,
Nadobnej Zosieńce
Pełny fartuszek.

"Ludzie będą myśleć
Żeś ty jaka pani.
Ty żeś sierota
Nad sierotami."

They muddied it, yes,
But when it settled,
Our pretty Sophie washed
Her kerchiefs in it.

She washed her kerchiefs;
John watered his horse.
"O Sophie, my dear one,
We are alone now.

"We are alone now;
We are of one heart.
Let us pick some cherries
From yonder orchard.

"We'll pick some cherries;
Some pears we'll pick too,
And fill the gay apron
Of pretty Sophie.

"And people will say,
'What a grand lady!'
E'en though you are poor, dear,
So poor and forlorn."

22

Słuchaj Chłopcze, Masz Mnie Kochać

LISTEN, MY BOY, LOVE ME YOU MUST

Con moto

Słu-chaj chłop - cze,   masz mnie ko - chać,
Lis - ten, my   boy,   love me you   must,

Ko - chać z du - szy ca - łej.   Ja nie bę - dę
Love me with   your whole soul.   I   will nev - er

pła - kać szlo - chać,   Jak in - ne szlo -
cry   and   blub - ber;   Oth - ers   may have

cha - ły. ___   Jak in - ne szlo - cha - ły.
blub - bered. ___   Oth - ers may have   blub-bered.

Sung in 1940 by Mrs. Sophia Dziob, who learned it from her sister
in Passaic, New Jersey.

Słuchaj chłopcze, masz mnie kochać,	*Listen, my boy, love me you must,*
Kochać z duszy całej.	*Love me with your whole soul.*
Ja nie będę płakać, szlochać,	*I will never cry and blubber;*
Jak inne szlochały.	*Others may have blubbered.*
Ja nie będę płakać, szlochać,	*I will never cry and blubber;*
Jak inne szlochały.	*Others may have blubbered.*

Pójdę w bory a tam mieszka
Czarownica stara.
Jak ona cię zaczaruje,
Napisze na niebie.
Potem z włosów twojej głowy
Pod krzyżem zagrzebie.

Kiedy puścisz się na wody,
Łódź z tobą zatonie.
Kiedy puścisz się na gody,
Roznoszą cię konie.
Kiedy puścisz się na gody,
Roznoszą cię konie.

Kiedy puścisz się na łowy,
Drzewo cię przewali.
A we żniwa w szczerym polu,
Piorun w cię wypali.
A we żniwa w szczerym polu,
Piorun w cię wypali.

A choć potem luby Stasio
Tak nie raz zapłacze,
"Przebacz, przebacz, droga Kasiu,"
A ja nie przebaczę.
"Przebacz, przebacz, droga Kasiu,"
A ja nie przebaczę.

I will go into the forest
Where an agèd witch lives.
When she casts a spell upon you,
She'll inscribe the heavens.
Then she'll take a lock of your hair,
'Neath the cross she'll bury it.

When you set sail on the waters,
Your boat will sink with you.
When a-calling you will go,
You will lose your way.
When a-calling you will go,
You will lose your way.

If you ever should go hunting,
A tall tree will fell you.
After harvest fields are barren,
You'll be struck by lightning.
After harvest fields are barren,
You'll be struck by lightning.

And though later, my dear Stanley,
You should beg and beg me,
"Dearest Katie, please forgive me,"
I will not forgive you.
"Dearest Katie, please forgive me,"
I will not forgive you.

23
Wedle Oświęcima Miasteczka
LOOK YE, NEAR THE TOWN OF OSWIECIM

Con moto

We - dle Oś - wię - ci - ma mias - tecz -
Look ye, near the town of Os - wie -

ka, We - dle Oś - wię - ci - ma mias - tecz -
cim, Look ye, near the town of Os - wie -

ka, Za - zie - le - ni - ła mi się,
cim, O how green, how ver - y green,

Za - zie - le - ni - ła mi się tra - wecz - ka.
O how green, how ver - y green grown the grass.

Sung in 1941 by Frank First, who learned it from a friend in
Pennsylvania.

Wedle Oświęcima miasteczka,	*Look ye, near the town of Oswiecim,*
Wedle Oświęcima miasteczka,	*Look ye, near the town of Oswiecim,*
Zazieleniła mi się,	*O how green, how very green,*
Zazieleniła mi się traweczka.	*O how green, how very green grows the grass.*
Zazieleniła mi się	*O how green, how very green,*
Zazieleniła mi się traweczka.	*O how green, how very green grows the grass.*

Koło tej traweczki gęsty las,
Nadybałem dziewczyne,
Nadybałem dziewczyne rozmawiać.

Ona rozmawiała, płakała,
"Czego Jasiu, mój Boże,
Czego Jasiu, mój Boże, doczekałam?"

"Hej, moja dziewczyno, nie smuć się.
Ja z wojenki powrócę,
Ja z wojenki powrócę, wezmę cię."

"A jak ty z wojenki powrócisz,
To mnie ty sierotynkę,
To mnie ty sierotynkę opuścisz."

"Hej, żebyś ty była sierota,
Nie miałabyś wianeczka,
Nie miałabyś wianeczka ze złota.

"Tylko byś go miała z liliji,
Jak to na sierotynkę,
Jak to na sierotynkę pasuje."

Near this meadow stands a forest dense.
There I stopped a maiden fair,
There I stopped a maiden fair for sweet talk.

She did talk and she did weep softly,
"O dear God! My dear Johnny!
O dear God! My dear Johnny! Grieved am I."

"Now there, my dear girl, be not so sad.
I'll return from battle fields,
I'll return from battle fields to claim you."

"But when you return from battle fields,
You'll forget an orphaned girl,
You'll forget an orphaned girl like poor me."

"Hey there! If you were an orphan poor,
Garlands you would never have,
Garlands you would never have of pure gold.

"You would have one made of lilies fair.
Such would suit a poor orphan,
Such would suit a poor orphan very well."

24

Ty Ze Mnie Szydzisz, Dziewucho

YOU ARE MAKING FUN OF ME, GIRL

Marcato

"Ty ze mnie szy-dzisz, dzie-wu-cho, Ty ze mnie szy-
"You are mak-ing fun of me, girl, Mak-ing fun of

dzisz. Ty mnie tyl-ko wten-czas ko-chasz Kie-dy mnie wi-
me. You on-ly pre-tend to love me When you are with

dzisz. Hop! hop! da-na da! Kie-dy mnie wi-dzisz
me. Hey! hey! da-na da! When you are with me,

da-da-na! Hop! hop! da-na da! Kie-dy mnie wi-dzisz."
da-da-na! Hey! hey! da-na da! When you are with me."

Sung in 1941 by Mrs. John Krupski, who learned it from a friend
in Buffalo.

"Ty ze mnie szydzisz, dziewucho,
Ty ze mnie szydzisz.
Ty mnie tylko wtenczas kochasz
Kiedy mnie widzisz.
Hop! hop! dana da!
Kiedy mnie widzisz, da dana!
Hop! hop! dana da!
Kiedy mnie widzisz."

"You are making fun of me, girl,
Making fun of me.
You only pretend to love me
When you are with me.
Hey! hey! dana da!
When you are with me, da dana!
Hey! hey! dana da!
When you are with me."

"Z ciebie nie szydzę, chłopaku,
Z ciebie nie szydzę.
Bo cię zawsze szczerze kocham
Choć cię nie widzę.
Hop! hop! dana da!
Choć cię nie widzę, da dana!
Hop! hop! dana da!
Choć cię nie widzę."

"Ty będziesz moją, dziewucho,
Ty będziesz moją.
Jeno mi się przysieweczki
Na polu dostoją.
Hop! hop! dana da!
Na polu dostoją da dana!
Hop! hop! dana da!
Na polu dostoją.

"Przysieweczki z pola sprzątnę
Wezmę wymłócę.
I zaniosę na zapowiedź,
Do ciebie wrócę.
Hop! hop! dana da!
Do ciebie wrócę, da dana!
Hop! hop! dana da!
Do ciebie wrócę.

"Jedną część dam organiście
By poszedł na chór
I zaśpiewał uroczyście
'Veni Creator.'
Hop! hop! dana da!
'Veni Creator,' da dana!
Hop! hop! dana da!
'Veni Creator.' "

"I do not make fun of you, boy,
I do not make fun,
For I always truly love you
Though I'm not with you.
Hey! hey! dana da!
Though I'm not with you, da dana!
Hey! hey! dana da!
Though I'm not with you."

"Yes indeed, you will be mine, girl,
Yes indeed, you will.
Just as soon as all my gold grain
Ripens in the field.
Hey! hey! dana da!
Ripens in the field, da dana!
Hey! hey! dana da!
Ripens in the field.

"I shall harvest all my gold grain,
I shall then thresh it.
I shall make my offering for banns
And return to you.
Hey! hey! dana da!
And return to you, da dana!
Hey! hey! dana da!
And return to you.

"One coin I'll give to the organist
To be in the choir.
Solemnly for us he will sing
'Veni Creator.'
Hey! hey! dana da!
'Veni Creator' da dana!
Hey! hey! dana da!
'Veni Creator.' "

25

Śpiewam Wesół Już Od Rana

MY SONG OF JOY BEGINS AT DAWN

(See number 26)

Moderato

Hej że da - na, mo - ja da - na! Śpie-wam we - sół
Hey da - na da - na, my da - na! My song of joy

już od ra - na. Krzy-żyk zna - czę na swem czo - le I z by-
be-gins at dawn. Rev-'rent-ly I cross my-self and To the

deł-kiem ru - szam w po - le. Gos-po-dy - ni chle - ba da - ła;
field I take my cat-tle. Ho, my mis-tress gives me my bread;

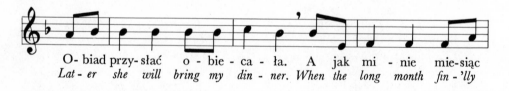

O- biad przy-słać o - bie - ca - ła. A jak mi - nie mie-siąc
Lat - er she will bring my din - ner. When the long month fin - 'lly

dłu - gi, Da ta - la - ra za za - słu - gi.
pass - es, For my work she'll pay a dol - lar.

Sung in 1940 by Mrs. Helen Poplawska, who learned it in Poland.

Hej że dana, moja dana!
Śpiewam wesół już od rana.
Krzyżyk znaczę na swem czole
I z bydełkiem ruszam w pole.
Gospodyni chleba dała;
Obiad przysłać obiecała.
A jak minie miesiąc długi,
Da talara za zasługi.

O mój Jezu, talar biały!
To mi-ci kram, to skarb cały
Kupić można na jarmarku!
Wszystkim przynieść coś w podarku.
Więc matuli chustkę krasną;
Basi śliczną wstążkę jasną;
Kaźmierkowi pas z kółkami,
I buty z podkówkami.

Lecz najpierwej wiem co zrobię;
Śliczny obraz kupię sobie,
Matkę Boską w gwiazd koronie,
Z Dzieciąteczkiem na jej łonie.
I wybiorę drzewo w lesie
Gdzie największy zapach niesie.
A kto w stronę tę pogoni
To Marji się pokłoni.

Hey dana dana, my dana!
My song of joy begins at dawn.
Rev'rently I cross myself and
To the field I take my cattle.
Ho, my mistress gives me my bread;
Later she will bring my dinner.
When the long month fin'lly passes,
For my work she'll pay a dollar.

O dear Jesus, a silver dollar!
O dear! O dear! what a fortune
One can barter at the town fair!
I'll buy gifts for everybody.
A gay kerchief for my mother;
A bright ribbon for sweet Barbara;
A fine studded belt for Casimer;
He'll have shoes with ringing heels, too.

But I know what I shall do first;
I shall buy a handsome picture
Of the Virgin crowned in starlight,
With the Holy Babe in her lap.
In the woods I'll choose a fine tree,
One whose fragrance is the sweetest.
Whosoe'er will travel that way
He will doff his cap to Mary.

26

Śpiewam Wesół Już Od Rana

MERR'LY I SING IN THE MORNING

(Variant of number 25)

Moderato

Hej - że da - na, mo - ja da - na!
Hey there da - na, da - na, da - na!

Śpie - wam we - sół już od ra - na;
Mer - r'ly I sing in the morn - ing;

Krzy - żyk zna - czę na swem czo - le
Sol - emn - ly I cross my - self and

I z by - deł kiem ru - szam w po - le.
Take my cat - tle to the pas - ture.

Sung in 1940 by Mrs. Jozefa Kochanowska, who learned it in Poland.

Hej-że dana, moja dana!
Śpiewam wesół już od rana;
Krzyżyk znaczę na swem czole
I z bydełkiem ruszam w pole.

Gospodyni chleba dała;
Obiad przysłać obiecała.
A jak minie miesiąc długi,
Da talara za zasługi.

Hey there dana, dana, dana!
Merr'ly I sing in the morning;
Solemnly I cross myself and
Take my cattle to the pasture.

Daily bread my mistress gives me;
To the field she brings my dinner.
When the long month slips by finally,
She gives me my dollar's wages.

27
Chłopek-ci Ja Chłopek
O I'M A PEASANT GAY

Sung in 1940 by Mrs. John Krupski, who learned it from her mother
in Buffalo.

Chłopek-ci ja chłopek,
W polu dobrze orzę.
Wszystko mi się dobrze dzieje,
Chwała Tobie Boże.
Wszystko mi się dobrze dzieje,
Chwała Tobie Boże.

Mam koniczków pare,
Cztery woły w pługu,
Chałupeczkę malusieńką
Bez wszelkiego długu.

O I'm a peasant gay,
I plow my land with ease.
Yes, everything goes well with me,
Glory be to Thee, God.
Everything goes well with me,
Glory be to Thee, God.

Horses I have a pair,
Four strong oxen in yoke.
My cottage small is cozy,
With no debts to vex me.

28

Ej Nieraz, Ja-ci Nieraz

HOW OFTEN, O HOW OFTEN

Giocoso

Ej nie - raz, ja - ci nie - raz, Ej
How of - ten, O how of - ten A -

przez tą rzecz - ke prze - lazł, Jesz - czem nie u to nął, u
cross this stream I've am - bled, Yet nev - er have I drowned, O

ha ha! Chy - ba - by ta____ te - raz,
ha ha! Un - less I do____ so now,

oj da - na! Jesz - czem nie u - to - nął, u ha ha!
O da - na! Yet nev - er have I drowned, O ha ha!

Chy - ba - by ta____ te - raz oj da - na!
Un - less I do____ so now, O da - na!

Sung in 1941 by Frank First, who learned it from his uncle,
who had learned it in Sonina, Poland.

"Ej nieraz, ja ci nieraz,
Ej przez tą rzeczke przelazł
Jeszczem nie utonął, u ha ha!
Chybaby ta teraz, oj dana!
Jeszczem nie utonął, u ha ha!
Chybaby ta teraz, oj dana!

"Ej widziałem cię dziewcze,
Ej w lesie cyprysowem,
Czesałaś se główke, u ha ha!
Grzebykiem perłowem, oj dana!

"Ej żeby mnie tu bili,
Ej bili i zabili,
To mi z tą dziewczyną, u ha ha!
Tańcować najmili, oj dana!

"Ej żeby mnie tu mieli
Ej porąbać, posiekać,
To się wolę bronić, u ha ha!
Niżeli uciekać, oj dana!

"Ej serce, moje serce,
Ej mówić do mnie nie chce.
Serce by gadało, u ha ha!
Ale dziewcze nie chce, oj dana!"

"Ej kochaj mnie albo nie,
Ej to na twojej woli;
Krzywo na mnie nie patrz, u ha ha!
Bo mnie serce boli, oj dana.

"Ej krzywo na mnie nie patrz,
Ej bom ci nic nie winna;
Kochać cię nie będę, u ha ha!
Bom cie nie powinna, oj dana!"

"Ej idzie wóz po za wóz,
Ej malowane luśnie.
Daj mi Maryś buzi, u ha ha!
Jak mamusia uśnie, oj dana!"

*"How often, O how often
Across this stream I've ambled,
Yet never have I drowned, O ha ha!
Unless I do so now, O dana!
Yet never have I drowned, O ha ha!
Unless I do so now, O dana!*

*"O once I saw you, lassie,
O in the cypress forest,
Combing your long tresses, O ha ha!
With a fine comb of pearl, O dana!*

*"O should they beat me sorely,
O beat me unto my death,
I still would swing this girl, O ha ha!
In this wild dance of joy, O dana!*

*"O should they ever try to
O chop away and mince me,
I'd fight them back fiercely, O ha ha!
Rather than run away, O dana!*

*"O sweetheart, my dear sweetheart:
No answer will she give me.
Her heart would speak gladly, O ha ha!
But O the girl will not, O dana!"*

*"O love me or ignore me,
O that is up to you, boy,
But do not be cross, O ha ha!
Because my heart is sore, O dana!*

*"O do not be cross with me,
O I have done you no wrong,
But love you I cannot, O ha ha!
For that I may not do, O dana!"*

*"O wagon upon wagon
Rides past with painted rundels,
Your kiss I'll have, Mary, O ha ha!
When Mamma falls asleep, O dana!"*

29

Kukułeczko, Gdzieżeś Wtenczas Była?[11]

LITTLE CUCKOO, WHERE, O WHERE
HAVE YOU BEEN?

Ku - ku - łecz - ko, gdzie żeś wten-czas by - ła?
Lit - tle cuck - oo, where, O where have you been?

Gdzie - żeś wten-czas by - ła? Cze - mu żeś mnie
Where, O where have you been? Why have you not

ra - no nie bu - dzi - ła? Ra - no nie bu - dzi - ła
wak - ened me this morn - ing Wak - ened me this morn - ing

Jak jam spał? Rum taj ra, rum taj ra,
When I slept? Rum tie rah, rum tie rah,

Rum - taj - ra, rum - taj - ra, Rum - ta - ra - ra -
Rum - tie - rah, rum - tie - rah, Rum - ta - rah - rah -

ra, Rum - taj ra, rum - taj - ra, Rum - taj - ra,
rah, Rum - tie - rah, rum tie - rah, Rum - tie - rah,

Sung in 1940 by Mrs. Helen Poplawska, who learned it from Professor
Edward Borkowski of Lwów, who collected folksongs from peasants
in the Province of Lublin, Poland.

Kukułeczko, gdzieżeś wtenczas była?   *Little cuckoo, where, O where have you been?*
Gdzieżeś wtenczas była?   *Where, O where have you been?*
Czemu żeś mnie rano nie budziła?   *Why have you not wakened me this morning,*
Rano nie budziła   *Wakened me this morning*
Jak jam spał?   *When I slept?*

Refren: Refrain:
Rum taj ra, rum taj ra,   *Rum tie rah, rum tie rah,*
Rum taj ra, rum taj ra,   *Rum tie rah, rum tie rah,*
Rum ta ra ra ra,   *Rum tah rah rah rah,*
Rum taj ra, rum taj ra,   *Rum tie rah, rum tie rah,*
Rum taj ra, rum taj ra,   *Rum tie rah, rum tie rah,*
Rum taj ra, rum ta ra ra ra,   *Rum tie rah, rum tah rah rah rah,*
Rum taj ra, rum ta ra ra,   *Rum tie rah, rum tah rah rah,*
Rum ta ra ra, rum ta ra ra,   *Rum tah rah rah, rum tah rah rah,*
Rum taj ra, rum ta ra ra,   *Rum tie rah, rum tah rah rah,*
Rum ta ra ra ra ra.   *Rum tah rah rah rah rah.*

30
Czemu Ty Płaczesz?[12]
WHY ARE YOU WEEPING?

Andante cantabile

"Cze - mu ty pła- czesz? Cze - mu ty
"*Why*   *are*   *you*   *weep - ing? Why*   *are*   *you*

pła - czesz, Dziew-czy - no   mo - ja?"   "Jak   nie
weep - ing, My   *be - lo - ed*   *girl?"*   *Why*   *should*

mam   ja   pła - kać?   Jak   nie mam   ża -
I   *not*   *weep?____ Why*   *should I*   *not*

ło - wać   Kie - dym   nie   two - ja?"
grieve____ Since   *we*   *now*   *must part?"*

Sung in 1940 by Mrs. Alexandra Szczepanik, who learned it in Poland.

"Czemu ty płaczesz?   "*Why are you weeping?*
Czemu ty płaczesz;   *Why are you weeping,*
Dziewczyno moja?"   *My beloved girl?"*
"Jak nie mam ja płakać?   "*Why should I not weep?*
Jak nie mam żałować   *Why should I not grieve*
Kiedym nie twoja?"   *Since we now must part?"*

"Będziesz ty moja,
Będziesz, dalibóg.
Ludzie mi cię rają,
Ojciec, matka dają,
I sam sądził Bóg.

"Ty będziesz panią
Przy wielkim dworze.
A ja będę księdzem
Księdzem kanonikiem
W wielkim klasztorze.

"Przed tobą będą
Czapki zdejmować.
A mnie jako księdza,
Księdza kanonika,
W rękę całować.

"Jak my pomrzemy,
Razem oboje,
Damy sobie wybić
Złote litery
Na swoim grobie.

"A kto tam pójdzie,
Przeczyta sobie
Złączona miłość,
Złączona miłość
Leży w tym grobie."

"*You will be mine,*
And God's will be done.
Folks have paired you with me,
I've your parents' blessing,
God be my witness.

"*You will be a lady*
In a fine mansion.
I shall be a priest,
A reverend canon
In a monastery.

"*Where'er you go,*
Men will doff their caps.
And my hand shall be
Kissed by all because of
My holy orders.

"*When we shall die,*
Both on the same day,
We shall have inscribed
Letters made of pure gold
Upon our grave.

"*They who will pass there*
Will read our tale
Of a love united,
Of a love united
Lying in this grave."

31

Nad Wodą Wieczornej Porze[13]
AT THE WATER'S EDGE ONE EV'NING

Nad wo - dą wie czor - nej po - rze, Za gą -
At the wa - ter's edge one ev' - ning, Watch - ing

ska - mi cho - dzi - ła Pa - ster - ka ślicz - na jak zo - rza
o'er her lit - tle geese, Fair as dawn this love - ly goose - girl

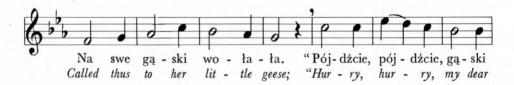

Na swe gą - ski wo - ła - ła. "Pój - dźcie, pój - dźcie, gą - ski
Called thus to her lit - tle geese; "Hur - ry, hur - ry, my dear

mo - je, Pój - dźcie, pój - dźcie, do do - mu. O - po - wiem wam
gos - lings, Hur - ry, hur - ry home with me. I shall tell — you

tros - ki mo - je; Nie po - wiedz - cie ni - ko - mu."
of my trou - bles; Pray do not re - veal my woe."

Sung in 1940 by Mrs. John Krupski, who learned it from friends
in Buffalo.

Nad wodą wieczornej porze,
Za gąskami chodziła
Pasterka śliczna jak zorza
Na swe gąski wołała.

Refren:
"Pójdźcie, pójdźcie gąski moje,
Pójdźcie, pójdźcie do domu.
Opowiem wam troski moje;
Nie powiedzcie nikomu.

"Jam w wolności się rodziła,
Choć nie znałam mej matki.
Temu sprzyjam komum miła,
Nie zwiodą mnie dostatki.

"Czy to zniesie moja dusza
Żebym temu sprzyjała
Który mnie właśnie przymusza
Żebym jego kochała?

"Niechaj kto chce wierzyć temu,
Jam me słowo raz dała,
Oddałam serce miłemu
I go będę kochała."

I tak chodząc za gąskami,
Rzewnie się rozpłakała.
Mając twarz zalaną łzami,
Na swe gąski wołała:

At the water's edge one ev'ning,
Watching o'er her little geese,
Fair as dawn, this lovely goosegirl
Called thus to her little geese:

Refrain:
"Hurry, hurry, my dear goslings,
Hurry, hurry home with me.
I shall tell you of my troubles;
Pray do not reveal my woe.

"I was born a child of freedom,
Though my mother I know not.
I do favor those who love me,
Nor am I beguiled by wealth.

"Can my heart endure the anguish
Of a love I do not feel
For the one who now compels me
To love no other but him?

"Let whoever will believe me,
I have pledged my love ere this.
And to him my heart is promised;
Him forever will I love."

And thus following her goslings,
Plaintively she wept this day.
With her tears her cheeks o'erflowing,
Thus she called her little geese:

32

Tam Na Cmentarzu

IN YONDER GRAVEYARD

Moderato

Tam na cmen - ta - rzu Przy ka - mie -
In yon - der grave - yard, Near a low

ni - ku, Klę - czy dziew-czy - na Tam przy pom -
mark - er, A maid is kneel - ing At a small

ni - ku. I tak se klę - czy I rzew- nie
tomb - stone. And as she kneels there, Bit - ter - ly

pła - cze, "Ko - gom ko - cha - ła Już nie zo -
she weeps, "Him that I have loved No more shall

1. ba czę." I tak se ba - **2.** czę."
I see." And as she I see."

Sung in 1941 by Frank First, who learned the song from his sister.
She had learned it in Sonina, Poland.

Tam na cmentarzu
Przy kamieniku,
Klęczy dziewczyna
Tam przy pomnikú.
I tak se klęczy
I rzewnie płacze,
"Kogom kochała
Już nie zobaczę."
I tak se klęczy
I rzewnie płacze,
"Kogom kochała
Już nie zobaczę."

I przyszedł do niej
Piękny młodzieniec.
"Komu dziewczyno
Wijesz ten wieniec?
Czy ci na wojnie
Zabili brata?
Albo ci ojciec
Zszedł z tego świata?"

"Ani mi w wojnie
Zabili brata,
Ani mi ojciec
Zszedł z tego świata,
Tylko mój luby
W tem grobie leży;
Ja grób kwiatami
Jego ozdobie."

"Czyliż na świecie
Nie ma młodzieży?
Tylko ten jeden
Co w grobie leży?"
"Chociaż na świecie
Wiele młodzieży,
Ja tego kocham
Co w grobie leży.

"Jednego w życiu
Chłopca kochałam.
Jednemu tylko
Swe serce dałam.
Chociaż na świecie
Wiele młodzieży
Ja tego kocham
Co w grobie leży."

In yonder graveyard,
Near a low marker,
A maid is kneeling
At a small tombstone.
And as she kneels there,
Bitterly she weeps,
"Him that I have loved
No more shall I see."
And as she kneels there,
Bitterly she weeps,
"Him that I have loved
No more shall I see."

A handsome stranger
Came to her this day.
"For whom, fair maiden,
Weave you that garland?
Was it a brother
You lost in battle?
Or has your father
By death been taken?"

"My brother has not
Been killed in battle,
Nor has my father
By death been taken,
But 'tis my sweetheart
Who lies here buried,
And with these flowers
I adorn his grave."

"Are there not other
Young men in this world?
Is he that lies here
The one man for you?"
"There may be many
Young men in this world,
But I love only
The one who lies here.

"Never have I loved
Any but this man.
Only to this one
My heart's devoted.
There may be many
Young men in this world,
But I love only
The one who lies here."

33
Za Górami[14]
OVER THE HILLS

Za gó - ra - mi, Za la - sa - mi
O - ver the hills, Be - yond the woods,

Tań - co - wa - ła Mał - go - rzat - ka
Mar - g'ret danced with great a - ban - don

1.
z hu - za - ra - mi.
With the hus - sars.

2.
za - ra - mi.
the hus - sars.

Sung in 1941 by Frank First, who did not remember from whom he had learned it. It is generally known by singers of Polish folksongs.

Za górami,	*Over the hills,*
Za lasami,	*Beyond the woods,*
Tańcowała Małgorzatka	*Marg'ret danced with great abandon*
Z huzarami.	*With the hussars.*
Tańcowała Małgorzatka	*Marg'ret danced with great abandon*
Z huzarami.	*With the hussars.*
Przysedł ojciec,	*Her father came;*
Przyszła matka.	*Her mother came.*
"Pójdź-że do dom, pójdź-że do dom,	*"Come home, O come home, do come home,*
Małgorzatko."	*Dear, dear Margaret."*

66

"Nie pójdę ja,
Idźcie sami.
Bo ja wolę potańcować
Z huzarami."

Tańcowała,
I płakała,
"Oj czego ja, oj czego ja
Doczekała?"

"I'll not come home.
Leave me alone.
I would rather, I would rather
Dance with hussars."

So on she danced,
And then she wept,
"O what ill fate, O what ill fate
Is my lot now?"

34

Wędrowała, Wędrowała

STROLLING SLOWLY, A TRIM MAIDEN

Moderato

Węd - ro - wa - ła, węd - ro - wa - ła
Stroll - ing slow - ly, a trim maid - en

Grze - czna pan - na dróż - ką.
Walked - a long a foot - path,

Na - tra - fi - ła lesz - czy - necz - kę
When she saw a ha - zel sap - ling,

Bar - dzo zie - lo - niuś - ką.
Ver - y, ver - y green 'twas.

Sung in 1941 by Mrs. John Krupski, who learned it from her mother
in Buffalo.

Wędrowała, wędrowała	*Strolling slowly, a trim maiden*
Grzeczna panna dróżką.	*Walked along a footpath,*
Natrafiła leszczyneczkę	*When she saw a hazel sapling,*
Bardzo zieloniuśką.	*Very, very green 'twas.*

"Powiedz-że mi, leszczyneczko,
Czemu się zielenisz?"
"Powiedz-że mi, panieneczko,
Czemu się czerwienisz?

"Bo ja stoję przy dolinie,
Temu się zielenie."
"A ja piję kawkę i miód,
Temu się czerwienię.

"A ja mam-ci siedmiu braci;
Każę ja cię zdradzić."
"Chociasz mnie zimą zdradzicie,
Na wiosnę wyrosnę.

"I tak sobie będę rosła,
Będę zieleniała,
A tyś wianek utraciła,
Nie będziesz go miała."

"Tell me now, wee hazel tree,
Why it is you grow green?"
"Will you tell me, my fair maiden
Why it is you blush so?

"I am growing in the valley,
That is why I grow green."
"Because I drink mead and coffee,
That is why I blush so.

"Know you I have seven brothers?
They will soon destroy you."
"Even though in winter I die,
I'll grow green when spring comes.

"And thus I shall go on growing,
Green and greener growing;
But your wreath you've lost forever,
Never to retrieve it."

35
Ludzkie Ogrody Się Zazieleniły
GREEN ARE THE GARDENS GROWING ALL AROUND ME

Ludz - kie o - gro - dy się za - zie - le - ni - ły;
Green are the gar - dens grow - ing all a - round me;

Mo - ja prze - nicz - ka nie wscho - dzi.
Wheat that I've sown, a - las, is not up.

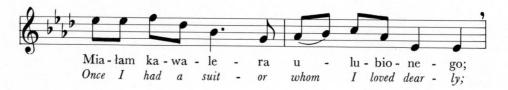

Mia - łam ka - wa - le - ra u - lu - bio - ne - go;
Once I had a suit - or whom I loved dear - ly;

Już te - raz do mnie nie cho - dzi.
I do not see him an - y more.

Sung in 1940 by Mrs. John Krupski, who learned it from her friends
in Buffalo.

Ludzkie ogrody się zazieleniły	*Green are the gardens growing all around me;*
Moja pszeniczka nie wschodzi.	*Wheat that I've sown, alas, is not up.*
Miałam kawalera ulubionego;	*Once I had a suitor whom I loved dearly;*
Już teraz do mnie nie chodzi.	*I do not see him any more.*

Albo mi go dajcie, albo mi go rajcie,
Albo mi życie odbierajcie.
Niech ja uboga nie żyje tu w tem
Tak wielkiem zmartwieniu.

Zostańcie z Bogiem, mili kawalerzy.
Dziś za kochanie dziękuję.
Jestem sobie wolna jak lilia polna.
Dziś do klasztoru wstępuję.

People, let me have him; let me see him now,
Or let this wretched life of mine end.
Orphan poor that I am, I should not suffer
Added afflictions in this world.

God rest you, gentlemen, charming though
I thank you kindly for your love. [you are;
I feel the sweet freedom, freedom of a lily.
Convent life will now be my love.

36

Szła Dziewczyna Koło Młyna

A GIRL WAS SAUNT'RING BY A MILL

Allegretto

Szła dziew - czy - na ko - ło mły -
A girl was saun - t'ring by a

na; Ro - bić się jej nie chce. _____ I
mill; She had no will for work. _____ She

spo - glą - da na sło - necz - ko Jak
looked up t'ward the sun to see How

wy - so - ko jesz - cze. _____ I cze. _____
high it still could be. _____ She be. _____

Sung in 1941 by Frank First, who learned it from his grandmother,
who had learned it in Sonina, Poland.

Szła dziewczyna koło młyna;	*A girl was saunt'ring by a mill;*
Robić się jej nie chce.	*She had no will for work.*
I spogląda na słoneczko	*She looked up t'ward the sun to see*
Jak wysoko jeszcze.	*How high it still could be.*
I spogląda na słoneczko	*She looked up toward the sun to see*
Jak wysoko jeszcze.	*How high it still could be.*

"Nie wysoko, nie daleko,
Chwała Panu Bogu."
Wzięła sobie poduszeczkę,
Poszła do ogrodu.

Poszła, poszła do ogrodu,
Trzy wianki uwiła.
Jeden sobie, drugi tobie
Trzeci powiesiła.

Powiesiła, powiesiła
W sieni za drzwierzami,
A gdy mama zobaczyła
Zalała się łzami.

"It is not high nor far away,
Thanks be to God above."
She fetched a pillow for her head
And to the garden went.

Into the garden green she went,
And wove three garlands fair.
The first was hers, the second yours,
The third she hung on high.

The third she hung, she hung on high
Behind a door at home,
And when her mother saw it there,
O woefully she wept.

37

Z Tamtej Strony Jeziora[15]

ON THE SHORE ACROSS THE LAKE

Energico

Z tam - tej stro - ny je - zio - ra,
On the shore a - cross the lake,

Sto - i lip - ka zie - lo - na. Hej! na tej
Stands a lit - tle lin - den tree. Hey! in this

lip - ce, Na tej zie - lo - nej,
lin - den, In this young green tree,

Trzej ptasz - ko - wie śpie - wa - ją.
Three fine birds are sing - ing there.

Sung in 1941 by Frank First, who learned it from his mother,
who had learned it in Sonina, Poland.

Z tamtej strony jeziora,	*On the shore across the lake,*
Stoi lipka zielona.	*Stands a little linden tree.*
Hej! na tej lipce,	*Hey! in this linden,*
Na tej zielonej,	*In this young green tree,*
Trzej ptaszkowie śpiewają.	*Three fine birds are singing there.*
Hej! na tej lipce,	*Hey! in this linden,*
Na tej zielonej,	*In this young green tree,*
Trzej ptaszkowie śpiewają.	*Three fine birds are singing there.*

Nie byli to ptaszkowie,	*O no birds are they, indeed,*

Nie byli to ptaszkowie,
Tylko kawalerowie.
Hej! zmawiali się
Do ładnej Marysi,
Któremu się dostanie.

Jeden mówi, "To moja!"
Drugi mówi, "Jak Bóg da!"
Hej! trzeci mówi,
"Maryniu moja,
Czemu mi taka smutna?"

"Jak że nie mam smutna być?
Za starego każą iść.
Zasmuciło się
Serduszko moje.
Nie mogę go utulić.

"A w tej nowej komorze
Stoi zielone łoże.
Hey! łoże, łoże
Piękne zielone,
Któż tam będzie na niem spał?

"A jak będzie stary spał,
Żeby do jutra nie wstał.
Jak będzie młody,
Pięknej urody,
Żeby mu Bóg zdrowie dał."

O no birds are they, indeed,
But three happy cavaliers.
Hey! they are vying for
Comely little Mary.
Which will be the lucky one?

"She is mine!" the first one said.
"We will see!" the second said.
But the third one asked,
"My little Mary,
Tell me why are you so sad."

"Why should I not woeful be?
I must marry an old man.
Heavy, so heavy
Is my poor young heart
And I cannot comfort it.

"In the new room over there,
Waiting is a green bedstead.
O bedstead, bedstead,
Beautiful bedstead,
Who, O who will sleep on it?

"If it should be an old man,
May he never see the dawn.
But if he be young,
Young and right handsome,
May God bless him with good health."

38
Przy Wielkiem Zamku
NEAR THE OLD TOWER

A ballad, sung in 1941 by Frank First, who learned it from his uncle
of Sonina, Poland.

Przy wielkiem zamku,	*Near the old tower*
Około wieży,	*Of a large castle,*
Gdzie młody żołnierz spoczywa;	*You'll see a soldier resting there.*
Tam młody żołnierz,	*This youthful soldier,*
Stojąc na warcie,	*While on guard duty,*
Taką piosenkę zaśpiewał;	*Oft sang a plaintive song like this:*

Tam młody żołnierz,
Stojąc na warcie,
Taką piosenkę zaśpiewał:

"Luby gołębiu,
Skróć me cierpienia;
Poleć mi w dalszą krainę
Gdzie moja luba
Teraz przebywa;
Przynieś mi od niej nowinę."

W tem młody gołąb
Z nowiną taką
Puścił się w dalszą krainę
Aby odwiedzać
Serce żołnierza
Od jego miłej dziewczyny.

"Młody żołnierzu,
Smutne twe troski;
Już inny twą słodycz pije.
Trzy lata mija
Jak twoja miła
Z innym młodzieńcem już żyje."

A młody żołnierz,
Z taką nowiną,
Bierze się o mur opiera.
Przystawia bagnet
Do piersi swojej,
I życie sobie odbiera.

This youthful soldier,
While on guard duty,
Oft sang a plaintive song like this:

"Dear dove that I love,
Shorten my suff'ring;
Fly to a distant land for me
Where my belovèd
Is now residing;
Return to me with news of her."

And so the young dove,
Bearing his message,
Flew to the distant land for him,
To bring glad tidings
To the lone soldier
From his belovèd in that land.

"O youthful soldier,
Sad is your burden,
Another's lips now drink your mead.
Three years have gone by
Since your dear loved one
Has found another youth to love."

So the young soldier,
Hearing the message,
Bolstered himself against the wall.
His bayonet fixed
Against his body,
He took his life and left this world.

39
Szeroki Mosteczek Ugina Się
THE LITTLE WIDE BRIDGE A BURDEN BEARS NOW

Sze - ro - ki mos-te - czek u - gi - na się,
The lit - tle wide bridge— a bur-den bears now,

Sze - ro - ki mos-te - czek u - gi - na się.
The lit - tle wide bridge —— a bur-den bears now,

Roś - nie na nim traw - ka; nie ko - si się,
Un - cut is the grass which is grow - ing there,

Roś-nie na nim traw - ka; nie ko-si - się.
Un - cut is the grass which is grow -ing there.

Sung in 1940 by Mrs. Sophia Dziob, who learned it in Tomaszowce.

Szeroki mosteczek ugina się,
Szeroki mosteczek ugina się.
Rośnie na nim trawka; nie kosi się,
Rośnie na nim trawka; nie kosi się.

Żeby ja ten mostek arendował,
Inaczej bym ja go ufundował.

The little wide bridge a burden bears now,
The little wide bridge a burden bears now.
Uncut is the grass which is growing there,
Uncut is the grass which is growing there.

Now if I had charge of this tiny bridge,
How diff'rently would I then arrange things.

Czerwone i białe róże sadzę;
Która panna ładna, odprowadzę.

Odprowadził bym ją aż do miasta.
Nieszczęśliwa patrol co mnie naszła.

Jak naszła tak naszła i zabrała.
Daleko na wojne odesłała.

Jak mi się na wojnie źle powiedzie,
Nakogoż narzekać jak nie na ciebie?

Na ciebie, na ciebie, na twoją mać,
Że mi cię nie chciała za żonę dać.

Za żonę, za żonę, za żonisię.
Wezmę karabinek, zastrzelę się.

O red and white roses I would plant there,
And any maid passing, I would escort.

Right up to the town I would escort her.
Alas! an ill-omened patrol met me.[16]

It met me, it met me, and it took me.
To far away battle they did send me.

And if I should fare ill while in battle,
On whom should I place the blame but you, girl.

On you girl, on you girl, and your mother,
Because, dear, she would not let me wed you.

Let me have you as my own little wife.
I will take my gun; I will shoot myself.

40

Po Deszczyku, Po Majowem

RAINDROPS FALLING GENTLY IN MAY

Moderato

Po deszc - czy - ku, po— Ma - jo - wem,
Rain -drops fall - ing gen - tly in May,

Tam gdzie wo - da z gó - ry pły - nie,
Wa - ter run - ning from— the hill - tops.

A ja w wian - ku li - li - -
With a gar - land made of—

jo - wem Cho - dzę so - bie po do - li - nie.
lil - ies, I oft wan - der o'er the val - ley.

Sung in 1941 by Mrs. Sophia Dziob, who learned this song in Passaic,
New Jersey.

Po deszczyku, po majowem	*Raindrops falling gently in May,*
Tam gdzie woda z góry płynie,	*Water running from the hilltops.*
A ja w wianku lilijowem	*With a garland made of lilies,*
Chodzę sobie po dolinie.	*I oft wander o'er the valley.*

Chodzę sobie po dolinie,	I oft wander through the green dale,
Czasem mazura zanucę;	Humming mazur tunes to myself,
Z słowikami się wyśpiewam,	Matching tunes with nightingale songs,
A z chłopcami się wykłócę.	Pouting coyly with the fellows.

I lilije i powoje,	All the lilies and the green vines,
I to moje i to moje.	These are all mine, all I survey.
I strumyki i potoki,	Rivers are mine, bubbling brooks too,
Wszystko moje, wszystko moje.	All are my own, all are my own.

Chodzę sobie po dolinie,	Once a lad walked through the green glade;
Napotkałem tam dziewczynę.	There he met a beautiful maid,
Spotkałem tam śliczną Zosię	There he chanced to meet fair Sophie
Co na wodę patrzyła się.	Sitting, gazing at the water.

Dzbankiem wodę nabierała	Drawing water, pitchers she filled,
I tak mazura śpiewała,	As she sang a mazur like this,
"Mazur-ci ja mazowiecki,	"A Mazovienne I am truly,
Starodawny, staroświecki.	Proud am I of my traditions.

"W Polsce ja się urodziła,	"I was born in Poland, fair land;
Polką moja matka była,	Poland born my mother was too.
Polska to jest kraj kochany,	Polish is the land belovèd
Spędziłam wiek młodociany."	Where I've spent sweet days of childhood."

41

Wszystkich To Ciekawość Budzi[17]

EV'RYBODY HAS BEEN WOND'RING

Giocoso

Wszyst-kich to cie - ka-wość bu - dzi Kto jest naj-szczęś-
Ev - 'ry-bod - y has been won-d'ring Who is for-tune's

liw-szy z lu - dzi, A ja my - ślę że ze sta-nów
fa - v'rite work - man. Now I think of all the sta - tions,

Naj-szczęś-liw - szy stan fur-ma-nów. Hej! wio!
That of coach-man is the fin - est Hey! vio!

het - ta wio! Het - ta, het - ta, het - ta wio!
het - ta vio! Het - ta, het - ta, het - ta vio!

Hej! wio! het-ta wio, Het-ta, het - ta, het-ta wio!
Hey! vio! het-ta vio, Het-ta, het - ta, het-ta vio!

Sung in 1941 by Mrs. John Krupski, who learned this song from a
friend in Buffalo.

Wszystkich to ciekawość budzi
Kto jest najszczęśliwszy z ludzi,
A ja myślę że ze stanów
Najszczęśliwszy stan furmanów.

Refren:
Hej! wio! hetta wio!
Hetta, hetta, hetta wio!
Hej! wio! hetta wio!
Hetta, hetta, hetta wio!

Biczek smukły, wozik kuty,
Konik dzielny, chomąt suty,
A smoły pełna maźnica.
Nie ma to jak pan woźnica.

Ev'rybody has been wond'ring
Who is fortune's fav'rite workman.
Now I think of all the stations,
That of coachman is the finest.

Refrain:
Hey! vio! hetta vio!
Hetta, hetta, hetta, vio!
Hey! vio, hetta vio!
Hetta, hetta, hetta vio!

Slender whipstock, four wheels well-rimmed,
Horse with spirit, harness sturdy,
Well greased wheels, smoothly turning;
Fortune's favorite is the coachman.

42

Oj Górol-ci Jo Górol

O I COME FROM THE HIGHLANDS

Adagio

Oj, gó - rol - ci jo gó - rol,
O I come from the high - lands,

Z pod sa - miuś - kich Ta - ter;
From the no - ble Ta - tras.

Oj, dys - cyk mnie wy -
O I've been bathed by

kom - poł, Wy - ko - ły - soł wio - ter.
rain - drops Rocked to sleep by high winds.

Sung in 1940 by Adam Bartosz, who learned this song in Poland.

Oj, górol-ci jo górol,	*O I come from the highlands,*
Z pod samiuśkich Tater;	*From the noble Tatras.*
Oj, dyscyk mnie wykompoł,	*O I've been bathed by raindrops,*
Wykołysoł wioter.	*Rocked to sleep by high winds.*
Oj, ani mi nie cięsko,	*O life is not a burden,*
Ani mi nie leko;	*Nor is life too easy;*
Oj, tylko mi do mojej	*'Tis only that the distance*
Dziewcyny daleko.	*To my girl is so great.*
Oj, góry, moje góry,	*O mountains, my own mountains,*
Cięsko mi za wamy.	*Lonesome am I for you.*
Oj, bo ja od maluśka	*O from my very childhood*
Naucały z wamy.	*Schooled have I been by you.*
Oj, Giwoniu, Giwoniu,	*O Giewont,[18] my dear Giewont,*
Cegoś tak osowioł?	*Why are you so hoary?*
Oj, cy cie mgły osiodły?	*O have the mists engulfed you?*
Cy cie wietsyk owioł?	*Have the winds enclosed you?*

II

When people are filled with laughter, they sing.
Their laughter can be carefree.
They applaud a witty girl with knowing laughter, or,
with melodic glee, a witty man.
Their laughter can be loud and strong, like the haw, haw,
haw of brassy horns.
Their laughter can be sharp, like newly broken glass,
splintered into swift narrow shafts.

43

Wesprzyj-że Mnie Boże[4]

HELP ME, LORD ALMIGHTY

(Variant of number 5)

Wes-przyj-że mnie, Bo - że, Wes-przyj - że mnie prze-cie.
Help me, Lord Al - might - y, Help me,   I im-plore you.

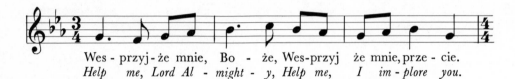

Wes - przyj-że mnie, Bo - że, Wes-przyj że mnie, prze - cie.
Help   me, Lord Al - might - y, Help me,   I im - plore you.

Bo mnie na   tym świe - cie Wiel-ka bie - da gnie - cie.
For I'm great - ly bur - dened In this world of   sor - rows.

Bo mnie na   tym świe - cie Wiel-ka bie - da gnie - cie.
For I'm great - ly bur - dened In this world of   sor - rows.

Sung in 1940 by Mrs. Sophia Dziob, who learned it from her husband,
who had learned it in Nowy Sącz, Poland.

Wesprzyj-że mnie, Boże,	*Help me, Lord Almighty,*
Wesprzyj-że mnie przecie.	*Help me, I implore you.*
Wesprzyj-że mnie, Boże,	*Help me, Lord Almighty,*
Wesprzyj-że mnie przecie.	*Help me, I implore you.*
Bo mnie na tym świecie	*For I'm greatly burdened*
Wielka bieda gniecie.	*In this world of sorrows.*
Bo mnie na tym świecie	*For I'm greatly burdened*
Wielka bieda gniecie.	*In this world of sorrows.*

Zakochałem-ci się	O in love I've fallen,
Aż po same uszy.	Lock and stock and barrel.
Rad bym pojąć Kaśkę,	Gladly would I wed Kate;
Rad bym z całej duszy.	All my heart's set on it.
Ale cóż tam z tego	But I can do nothing
Kiej psiadusza Kaśka	Since that meany, Katie,
Co spojrzy raz na mnie,	For each glance she gives me,
Dwa razy na Jaśka.	Glances twice at Johnny.
Wiem-ci ja co zrobię	Now I know what I'll do:
Pójdę za wojaczka.	I'll become a soldier;
Będę se wywijał	And my sword I'll brandish
Szabelką z półroczka.	O at least for six months.
A jak mi się szczęście	When the wheel of fortune
I potoczy kołem,	Turns its favors my way,
To może se stanę	Then perhaps I shall be
Panem jenerałem.	An exalted general.
Jak pojadę przez wieś	When upon my grey horse
Na siwem koniku,	I ride through the village,
Pojedzie też za mną	Lads will ride behind me,
Chłopaków bez liku.	Multitudes in number.
Jak Kaśka zobaczy	And when Katie sees me,
Pana jenerała,	An exalted general,
Będzie też to za mną	She will love me madly,
Szalała, szalała.	Madly, very madly.
Ja się najpierw zgniewam,	First I will be angry,
Ale później zmięknę,	Then I'll soften somewhat;
I z moją Kasieńką	And with my dear Katie
Do ołtarza klęknę.	At the altar I'll kneel.
A Jaśka psiajuchę	As for John, the villain,
Wezmę za pastucha.	He will be my swineherd.
Niech się memu szczęściu	Let him be a witness
Napatrzy, nasłucha.	To my wond'rous fortune.
A jak nas Pan Jezus	And when our Lord Jesus
Obdarzy dziatkami,	Blesses us with children,
Będą takie ładne	They will be as handsome
Jako i my sami.	E'en as we ourselves are.

44
Oj Nie Chcę Cię Kasiu[19]
I'LL NOT HAVE YOU, KATIE

Energico

"Oj nie chcę cię Ka-siu, Nie chcę cię. Bo o to-
"I'll not have you, Ka-tie, I will not. For peo-ple

bie lu-dzie Mó-wią źle. Że ra-no nie wsta-jesz; By-
are talk-ing Ill of you. You do not rise ear-ly; You

deł-ku nie da-jesz; Cze-lad-ki nie bu-dzisz; Sa-
do not feed the cows; The help you do not wake; You

ma się nie chłu-dzisz. Oj! nie! nie! nie!"
do not keep ti-dy. O no! no! no!"

Sung in 1941 by Adam Bartosz, who learned it from villagers in Poland.

"Oj nie chcę cię Kasiu,
Nie chcę cię.
Bo o tobie ludzie
Mowią źle.
Że rano nie wstajesz;
Bydełku nie dajesz;
Czeladki nie budzisz;
Sama się nie chłudzisz.
O nie! nie! nie!"

"I'll not have you, Katie,
I will not.
For people are talking
Ill of you.
You do not rise early;
You do not feed the cows;
The help you do not wake;
You do not keep tidy.
O no! no! no!"

"Nie prawda, Jasiuniu,
Nie prawda.
Kto ci to powiedział
Wart diabła.
Bo ja rano wstaję;
I bydełku daję;
I czeladki budzę;
I sama się chłudzę.
Oj tak! tak! tak!

"A jak mi nie wierzysz,
Miluśki,
Przywiąż mi dzwoneczek
Do nóżki.
Jak będę wstawała,
To będę dędała;
Jak będę chodziła,
To będę dzwoniła.
Dyn, dyn, dyn."

Posłuchał Jasiunio
Niebogi.
Przywiązał jej dzwonek
Do nogi.
Kasieńka leżała,
I nóżką ruszała,
A Jasiunio myślał
Że tak pracowała.
Oj tak! tak! tak!

"*That is not true, Johnny,*
No, not true.
Whoe'er said that is worth
The devil.
I surely rise early;
I feed the cows daily;
I waken the farmhands;
I keep myself tidy.
O yes! yes! yes!

"*If you don't believe me,*
My darling,
Then do tie a bell to
My ankle.
When I rise each morning,
I will ring ding-a-ling.
Wherever I do walk,
I will ring ding-a-ling.
Yes, ding-a-ling."

And so Johnny, the wretch,
Believed her,
And he tied a bell to
Her ankle.
And Katie lay abed
And shook her little leg,
And poor Johnny was sure
That Katie was working.
O yes! yes! yes!

45

Kąpała Mnie Mama We Wodzie

MY MOTHER BATHED ME IN CLEAR WATER

Moderato

Ką - pa - ła mnie ma - ma we wo - dzie
My moth - er bathed me in clear wa - ter;

A - że - bym był ład - ny w u - ro - dzie.
She want - ed me hand - some and charm - ing.

Ką - pa - ła mnie ma - ma w ba - li - ji
My moth - er bathed me in a wash - tub;

Że - by mnie dziew - czę - ta lu - bi - ły. lu - bi - ły.
She want - ed the girls to ad - mire me. ad - mire me.

Sung in 1941 by Frank First, who learned it from his mother,
who had learned it in Sonina, Poland.

Kąpała mnie mama we wodzie	*My mother bathed me in clear water;*
Ażebym był ładny w urodzie.	*She wanted me handsome and charming.*
Kąpała mnie mama w baliji	*My mother bathed me in a washtub;*
Żeby mnie dziewczęta lubiły.	*She wanted the girls to admire me.*
Kąpała mnie mama w baliji	*My mother bathed me in a washtub;*
Żeby mnie dziewczęta lubiły.	*She wanted the girls to admire me.*

Kąpała mnie mama w leszczynie
Żebym się spodobał dziewczynie.
Kąpała mnie mama w Dunaju
Za to mnie panienki kochają.

Pytała się ptaszka na pniaku
Czy też wolno kochać chłopaków.
"A wolno, a wolno, cóż by nie?
Za chłopaków grzechów nie ma, nie."

Napisali ludzie do nieba
Czy też także kochać potrzeba.
A Pan Bóg im na to ze złością,
"Kiedy każdy żyje miłością."

In a hazel grove she did bathe me;
She wanted the girls to approve me.
In the River Danube she bathed me;
She wanted the maidens to love me.

A maid asked a bird on a tree stump
If loving the boys was permitted.
"Aye, it is permitted, and why not?
Boys, too, are God's creatures, my dear lass."

So people sent letters to heaven
To see whether love was essential.
Angered justly, God answered them thus,
"All men should live only by true love."

46
A Co To Tam Stuknęło?[20]
WHAT'S THE TAPPING THAT I HEAR?

Sung in 1940 by Mrs. John Krupski, who learned it from her mother in Buffalo.

A co to tam stuknęło?
A co to tam puknęło?
Pewnie komar z dębu spadł,
Złamał sobie w krzyżu gnat.

What's the tapping that I hear?
What's the knocking that I hear?
A mosquito tumbled down
From the oak and broke its crown.

Dowiedziała się mucha
Że już komar bez ducha.
Pyta jednak komara
Czy potrzeba doktora.

And the fly soon heard the news:
The mosquito's soul had fled.
None the less, she asked of it,
If a doctor should be called.

Nie potrzeba doktora;
Nie pomoże tu smara.
Raczej rydel, motyka
Lepsza niżli apteka.

Do not call the doctor now;
No massage will be of help.
Rather get a pick and spade
Than the aid of any drug.

92

Był więc pogrzeb wspaniały;
Wszystkie muchy płakały;
I dla smutku wielkiego
Nie lyzały słodkiego.

I śpiewały rekwie
Że już komar nie żyje.
W końcu na ladacie
Zjadły z miodu kolację.

So a funeral was arranged.
All the flies wept daintily.
And for proper mourning's sake,
They refrained from licking sweets.

And they sang a requiem;
The mosquito's death proclaimed.
In the end upon a chest
On pure honey they did dine.

47
Tam na Błoniu Błyszczy Kwiecie
IN THE MEADOW FLOWERS GLISTEN

(See number 48)

Tam na bło-niu błysz-czy kwie-cie, Sto-i u-łan
In the mead-ow flow-ers glis-ten; Stand-ing guard, a

na wi-de-cie, A dziew-czy-na, jak ma-li-na,
sol-dier watch-es As a young girl with her ros-es

Nie-sie ko-szyk róż; A dziew-czy-na,
Tries to pass that way; As a young girl

jak ma-li-na, Nie-sie ko-szyk róż.
with her ros-es Tries to pass that way.

Sung in 1941 by Frank First, who learned it while singing with a
Polish choir in Detroit.

Tam na błoniu błyszczy kwiecie,	*In the meadow flowers glisten;*
Stoi ułan na widecie,	*Standing guard, a soldier watches*
A dziewczyna, jak malina,	*As a young girl with her roses*
Niesie koszyk róż;	*Tries to pass that way;*
A dziewczyna, jak malina,	*As a young girl with her roses*
Niesie koszyk róż.	*Tries to pass that way.*

"Stój! Poczekaj, moja duszko.
Gdzie tak drobną stąpasz nóżką?"
"Jam z tej chatki rwała kwiatki
I powracam już."

"Próżne twoje są wymówki;
Pójdziesz ze mną do placówki."
"Ach ja biedna sama jedna!
Matka czeka mnie."

"Stąd wrogi są o pół mili.
Pewnie ciebie namówili."
"Ach dla Boga! Nigdym wroga
Nie widziała, nie!"

"Może kryjesz wrogów tłuszcze.
Daj buziaka to cię puszczę."
"Jam nie taka. Dam buziaka,
Tylko z konia zsiądź."

"Z konia zsiądę, prawo złamie,
Za to kulą w łeb dostanę."
"Jakiś prędki! Dość twej chętki!
Bez buziaka bądź!"

"Choć mnie życie ma kosztować,
Muszę ciebie pocałować."
"Żal mi ciebie, jak Bóg w niebie,
Bo się zgubisz sam."

"A jak wartę mą porzucę
I szczęśliwie z wojny wrócę?"
"Bądź spokojny; wrócisz z wojny
Pocałunek dam."

"Jak szczęśliwie wrócę z boju,
Gdzie cię szukać mam w pokoju?"
"Tu w tej chatce przy mej matce,
Nad tą rzeczką w wyż."

"A jak zginę, co tak snadnie,
To buziaczek mi przepadnie."
"Wiernam tobie, na twem grobie
Pocałuję krzyż."

"Halt! One moment! My dear pigeon,
Where to, with such mincing footsteps?"
"I am come from yonder cottage
Where these roses grow."

"Useless is your explanation;
To the outpost follow me, lass."
"Woe unto me! I am alone.
My poor mother waits."

"Half mile down the foe is stationed.
Doubtless they have sent you spying."
"God's my witness, ne'er have I seen
Enemies about."

"Ha! I wager you do shield them.
Kiss me, girl, and you will go free."
"Do not judge me. I will kiss you.
First you should dismount."

"I would break rules, should I dismount;
My reward would be a bullet."
"What a hero! Nought I'll give you.
Live without my kiss."

"Even though it costs me my life,
I'll not sacrifice your sweet kiss."
"God's my witness, you've my pity.
You'll destroy yourself."

"Should I ever leave this duty
And return from battle safely?"
"Rest in peace, whene'er you come back,
You will have your kiss."

"And when I return from battle,
Where will I then find you, my girl?"
"In yon cottage, near the river,
With my mother dear."

"Should I lose my life in battle,
Your sweet kiss I'll lose forever."
"Faithful to you, on your tombstone,
I shall plant a kiss."

48

Tam na Błoniu Błyszczy Kwiecie

IN THE MEADOW FLOWERS GLISTEN

(Variant of number 47)

Allegretto

Tam na bło - niu błysz - czy kwie - cie,
In the mead - ow flow - ers glis - ten;

Sto - i u - łan na wi - de - cie, A dziew - czy - na
Stand - ing guard, a sol - dier watch - es As a young girl

jak ma - li - na, Nie - sie ko - szyk róż.
with her ros - es Tries to pass that way.

Sung in 1941 by Mrs. John Krupski, who learned it in Buffalo.

Polish and English texts are similar to those in number 47.

49
Słomą Krytej, W Niskiej Chatce
IN A THATCH-ROOFED LITTLE COTTAGE

Moderato

Sło - mą kry - tej, w nis - kiej chat - ce,
In a thatch - roofed lit - tle cot - tage,

Przy u - bo - giej miesz - kam mat - ce. Przyjdż - cie
With my dear, poor moth - er I live. Call on

do nas, zo - ba - czy - cie Ja - kie u nas
us and you will no - tice That our life is

mi - łe ży - cie. Ko - ło - wro - tek się o -
ver - y pleas - ant. Hear the spin - ning wheel turn

bra - ca; U - bós - two nam ży cie skra - ca.
smooth - ly. Pov - er - ty our lives does short - en.

Sung in 1941 by Mrs. John Krupski, who learned it from her sister in Buffalo.

Słomą krytej, w niskiej chatce,
Przy ubogiej mieszkam matce.
Przyjdżcie do nas zobaczycie
Jakie u nas miłe życie.
Kołowrotek się obraca;
Ubóstwo nam życie skraca.

In a thatch-roofed little cottage,
With my dear, poor mother I live.
Call on us and you will notice
That our life is very pleasant.
Hear the spinning wheel turn smoothly.
Poverty our lives does shorten.

50

Pognała Wółki[21]

SHE DROVE HER OXEN

Allegretto

Pog - na - ła wół - ki Na bu - ko - wi - ne.
She drove her ox - en In - to the beech grove,

Wzie - ła ze so - bą Skrzyp - ce je - dy - ne
And with her she brought Her treas-ured fid - dle.

Tam gra - ła, śpie - wa - ła, Swo - je
There she— fid - dled and sang, While she

sza - re si - we Wół - ki pa - sa - ła.
watched and tend - ed Her grey, grey ox - en.

Sung in 1940 by Mrs. Sophia Dziob, who learned it in Tomaszowce, Poland.

Pognała wółki	*She drove her oxen*
Na bukowinę.	*Into the beech grove,*
Wzięła ze sobą	*And with her she brought*
Skrzypce jedyne.	*Her treasured fiddle.*
Tam grała, śpiewała,	*There she fiddled and sang,*
Swoje szare siwe	*While she watched and tended*
Wółki pasała.	*Her grey, grey oxen.*

Tam grała, śpiewała,
Swoje szare siwe
Wółki pasała.

Oj, pasała, pasała
I pogubiła.
Cóż ja nieszczęsna
Będę robiła?
I chodzi i płacze,
"Pewnie swoje siwe
Wółki utracę."

Usłyszał Janek
Płacz, narzekanie.
Przyleciał zara
Na te wołanie.
"Dziewczyno, co ci to?
Pewnie twoje szare
Wółki zajęto."

"Oj żebyś ty mi
Wółki odnalazł,
Dała ja bym ci
Całusa zaraz."
"Jak zaraz tak zaraz,
Siedemdziesiąt siedem
Razy, raz po raz."

Poleciał Janek
Na bukowine.
Odnalazł wółki
Wółki jedyne.
"Dziewczyno, wółki masz.
Obiecałaś dać buziaka;
Daj zaraz."

"Dała ja bym ci
Z największej chęci,
Ale się mama
Po sieni kręci."
"Dziewczyno szachrajko,
Obiecałaś a nie
Dałaś, cyganko!"

There she fiddled and sang
While she watched and tended
Her grey, grey oxen.

Thus she did watch them
Until she lost them.
"O hapless am I!
What will I do now?"
So she searched, and she cried,
"Surely now I have lost
My grey, grey oxen."

Johnny heard her thus
Crying, complaining.
He hurried right off
To do what he could.
"Girl, what is your trouble?
Your grey oxen, doubtless,
Have been impounded."

"If you would only
Find my grey oxen,
How promptly would I
Give you a kiss."
"If promptly, then right now,
Seventy-seven times
In sweet succession."

Right smartly Johnny
Ran to the beech grove.
He found the oxen,
Highly prized oxen.
"Now you have your oxen.
A kiss you have promised.
Give it to me now."

"Surely I'd kiss you'
Willingly, I say,
But I hear Mamma
Moving about."
"Girl, you are a rascal!
You do not keep your word.
O what a fibber!"

51

Pojedziemy Na Łów, Na Łów[22]

WE SHALL GO A-HUNTING, HUNTING

Energico

Po - je - dzie - my na łów, na łów,
We shall go a - hunt - ing, hunt - ing,

To - wa - rzy - szu mój, To - wa - rzy - szu
My de - vot - ed friend, My de - vot - ed

mój, Na łów, na łow, na ło - wy, Do zie - lo - nej
friend, Hunt - ing, hunt - ing, a - hunt - ing To the green oak

dąb - ro - wy, To - wa - rzy - szu mój. mój.
for - est glade, My de - vot - ed friend. friend.

last verse

Sung in 1940 by Mrs. John Krupski, who learned it from her mother, who had learned it from a friend in Buffalo.

Pojedziemy na łów, na łów,	*We shall go a-hunting, hunting,*
Towarzyszu mój,	*My devoted friend,*
Towarzyszu mój,	*My devoted friend,*
Na łów, na łów, na łowy,	*Hunting, hunting, a-hunting*
Do zielonej dąbrowy,	*To the green oak forest glade,*
Towarzyszu mój.	*My devoted friend.*

A tam biegnie zając, zając,
Towarzyszu mój,
Towarzyszu mój.
Puszczaj charty ze smyczą;
Niech zająca pochwycą,
Towarzyszu mój.

Ho! There goes a rabbit, rabbit,
My devoted friend,
My devoted friend.
Let us set the greyhounds free;
They will fetch the rabbits here,
My devoted friend.

A tam biegnie sarna, sarna,
Towarzyszu mój,
Towarzyszu mój.
Puszczaj charty ze smyczą;
Niechaj sarnę pochwycą,
Towarzyszu mój.

Ho! There goes a reindeer, reindeer,
My devoted friend,
My devoted friend.
Let us set the greyhounds free;
They will fetch the reindeer here,
My devoted friend.

A tam biegnie sobol, sobol,
Towarzyszu mój,
Towarzyszu mój,
Puszczaj charty ze smyczą;
Niech sobola pochwycą,
Towarzyszu mój.

Ho! There goes a sable, sable,
My devoted friend,
My devoted friend.
Let us set the greyhounds free;
They will fetch the sable here,
My devoted friend.

A tam biegnie panna, panna,
Towarzyszu mój,
Towarzyszu mój.
Puszczaj charty ze smyczą;
Niechaj pannę pochwycą,
Towarzyszu mój.

Ho! There goes a maiden, maiden,
My devoted friend,
My devoted friend.
Let us set the greyhounds free;
They will fetch the maiden here,
My devoted friend.

A teraz się dzielmy, dzielmy,
Towarzyszu mój,
Towarzyszu mój.
Tobie zając, i sarna,
A mnie sobol i panna,
Towarzyszu mój.

Let's divide the booty, booty,
My devoted friend,
My devoted friend.
Rabbit and the deer for you,
Sable and the girl for me,
My devoted friend.

A kiedy ci krzywda, krzywda,
Towarzyszu mój,
Towarzyszu mój,
Moja szabla a twój kij,
Teraz-że się ze mną bij,
Towarzyszu mój.

If you deem this unjust, unjust,
My devoted friend,
My devoted friend,
You can have it out with me;
Match your staff against my sword,
My devoted friend.

52
Chciało Się Zosi Jagódek
SOPHIE WAS CRAVING BERRIES RIPE

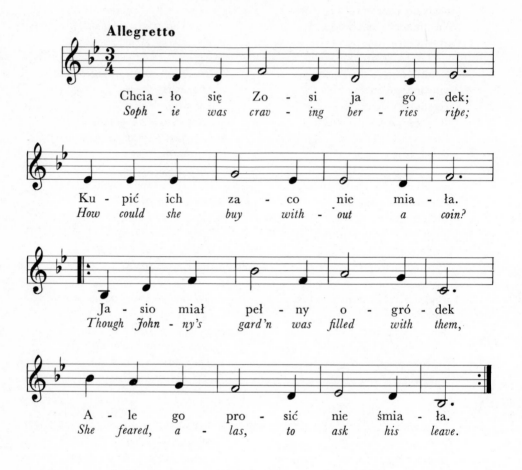

Allegretto

Chcia - ło się Zo - si ja - gó - dek;
Soph - ie was crav - ing ber - ries ripe;

Ku - pić ich za - co nie mia - ła.
How could she buy with - out a coin?

Ja - sio miał peł - ny o - gró - dek
Though John - ny's gard'n was filled with them,

A - le go pro - sić nie śmia - ła.
She feared, a - las, to ask his leave.

Sung in 1941 by Frank First, who could not recall just where he had
first heard it or from whom he had learned it.

Chciało się Zosi jagódek;	*Sophie was craving berries ripe;*
Kupić ich zaco nie miała.	*How could she buy without a coin?*
Jasio miał pełny ogródek	*Though Johnny's gard'n was filled with them,*
Ale go prosić nie śmiała.	*She feared, alas, to ask his leave.*
Jasio miał pełny ogródek	*Though Johnny's gard'n was filled with them,*
Ale go prosić nie śmiała.	*She feared, alas, to ask his leave.*

Wnet sobie sposób znalazła.
Rankiem się z chatki wykradła;
Cicho przez płotek przelazła;
Jasiowi wiśnie objadła.

Poznał się Jasio na szkodzie.
"Wróble to," mówi, "zrobiły."
Postawił stracha w ogrodzie.
"Nie będą odtąd gościły."

Zosia się stracha nie bała.
Szczęśliwie płotek przelazła;
Z swojej się sztuki naśmiała
I nową szkodę zrobiła.

Ale się Jasio domyślał
Co za ptaszeczek tak śmiały.
Nowe sidełka przemyślał
I nie źle mu się udały.

Na miejsce tyczki złamanej
Cicho pod drzewem sam staje.
Wziął na się stare łachmany
I niby stracha udaje.

Zosia swym dawnym zwyczajem
Z cicha gałązki nagina.
"A tuż mi miły hultaju!"
Złapana była dziewczyna.

However, she soon found a way.
At dawn she stole from her cottage;
Quietly she climbed o'er the fence;
On Johnny's berries she feasted.

Johnny soon noticed the damage.
"The work of sparrows," he declared.
He placed a scarecrow in the patch.
"They will not call again," he said.

The scarecrow did not stop Sophie.
The fence she climbed without mishap
And gaily laughed at her sly prank
As she resumed the plunder sweet.

Now Johnny soon surmised the type
Of bird that boldly stole his fruit.
He planned another kind of trap
Which turned out rather well for him.

The broken pole he threw aside
And took his place beneath a tree.
In tattered rags he dressed himself,
Feigning a scarecrow now to be.

Sophie, as was her habit now,
Cautiously at the branches pulled.
"Ah ha! my little sweet rascal!"
And thus the girl was trapped by him.

53
A Tam W Krakowie We Młynie
YONDER IN KRAKOW IN A MILL

A tam w Kra - ko - wie we mły -
Yon - der in Kra - kow in a

nie, A tam w Kra - ko - wie we mły - nie.
mill, Yon - der in Kra - kow in a mill,

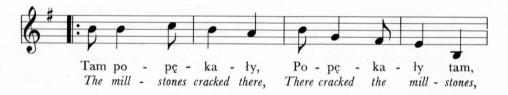

Tam po - pę - ka - ły, Po - pę - ka - ły tam,
The mill - stones cracked there, There cracked the mill - stones,

Tam po - pę - ka - ły ka - mie - nie.
The mill - stones cracked there in the mill.

Sung in 1941 by Frank First, who learned it while picnicking in Detroit.

A tam w Krakowie we młynie,	*Yonder in Krakow in a mill,*
A tam w Krakowie we młynie,	*Yonder in Krakow in a mill,*
Tam popękały,	*The millstones cracked there,*
Popękały tam,	*There cracked the millstones,*
Tam popękały kamienie.	*The millstones cracked there in the mill.*
Tam popękały,	*The millstones cracked there,*
Popękały tam,	*There cracked the millstones,*
Tam popękały kamienie.	*The millstones cracked there in the mill.*

Młynarczyk będzie naprawiał.
Kawaler panne,
Panne kawaler,
Kawaler panne namawiał.

"Pojadę, Kasiu, dalej w świat.
Ty będziesz ze mną,
Ze mną ty będziesz,
Ty będziesz ze mną wędrować."

Przywędrowali w gęsty las.
"Tu będziem, Kasiu,
Kasiu, tu będziem,
Tu będziem, Kasiu spoczywać.

"Ty myślisz, Kasiu, że ja śpię.
Ja myśli twoje,
Twoje ja myśli,
Ja myśli twoje rozumiem."

"Kto moje myśli rozumie,
Na wojnie niechaj,
Niechaj na wojnie,
Na wojnie niechaj zaginie."

The miller will soon repair them.
A lad his lassie,
His lassie a lad,
A lad his lassie was wooing.

"Kate, I will ride to see the world.
You will go with me,
With me you will go,
You will go with me, my dear Kate."

And when they came to a dark wood,
"Katie, here we shall,
Here we shall, Katie,
Katie, here we shall rest a while.

"You think that I am sleeping, Kate.
I know your thoughts, dear,
Your thoughts I know, dear,
I know your thoughts, dear, very well."

"Whoever thinks he knows my thoughts,
In battle may he,
May he in battle,
In battle may he be destroyed."

54
Szło Sobie Dwóch Dziadów
TWO OLD BEGGARS STAGGERED

Allegretto

Szło so - bie dwóch dzia-dów Po u - bi - tej
Two old beg-gars stag-gered Down a beat-en

szo - sie; Pi - ja - ki, łaj - da - ki, Ob - dar -
high - way; Rep - ro - bates and drunk - ards, Bare of

te i bo - se. Karcz - me zo - ba -
foot and tat - tered. When they saw a

czy - li, Tak so - bie mó - wi - li, "Bie - da,
tav - ern, Thus the two la - ment - ed, "Too bad!

gro - sza nie - ma! Wód - ki byś - my pi - li."
Not a pen - ny! We could use some vod - ka."

Sung in 1940 by Mrs. Bernice Mochocka, who learned it in
Dziektazewo, Poland.

Szło sobie dwóch dziadów
Po ubitej szosie;
Pijaki, łajdaki,
Obdarte i bose.
Karczmę zobaczyli,
Tak sobie mówili,
"Bieda, grosza niema!
Wódki byśmy pili."

Ogląda się jeden,
Widzi że pan jedzie;
Mówi do drugiego,
"Zaraz wódka będzie.
Kładź się ty na szosie
Tak jak byś nie słyszał,
A jak pan nadjedzie,
Byś wcale nie dyszał."

Pan serca dobrego
Pyta co się stało.
"Ach panie drogi,
Widzisz martwe ciało.
A już z tego miejsca
Na krok się nie ruszę;
Będę pokutował
Za te zmarłe dusze."

Pan serca dobrego
Grosza nie żałował;
Sięgnął do kieszeni,
Rubla podarował.
Pan na bryczkę siada,
Lejce w ręce chwyta;
Umarły żywego
O jałmużnę pyta.

Two old beggars staggered
Down a beaten highway;
Reprobates and drunkards,
Bare of foot and tattered.
When they saw a tavern,
Thus the two lamented,
"Too bad! Not a penny!
We could use some vodka."

One looked all about him;
Saw a fine man riding;
And he told his partner,
"We will have our vodka.
Lie down on the highway
As if you could hear nought.
When his lordship rides up,
Hold your breath in tightly."

Then the man of good will
Asked them what had happened.
"Now alas, my kind sir.
You see he is dead, sir.
Not a step will I move
From this wretched spot, sir,
But here do my penance
For the soul departed."

Then the man of good will
Gen'rous with his money,
Reached into his pocket,
Offered him a ruble.
He went to his britzka,
Took the reins in his hands,
While the "dead" one asked the
Living one for his share.

55
Widziałem Marysie Raz We Młynie
I ONCE SAW FAIR MARY IN THE GRIST MILL

Allegretto

Wi - dzia - łem Ma-ry - sie raz we mły - nie,
I once saw fair Ma - ry in the grist mill,

Wi - dzia - łem Ma - ry - sie raz we mły - nie,
I once saw fair Ma - ry in the grist mill,

Jak la - zła na gó - re po dra - bi - nie,
As up - ward and up the lad - der she climbed,

Jak la - zła na gó - re po dra - bi - nie.
As up - ward and up the lad-der she climbed.

Sung in 1940 by Mrs. Sophia Dziob, who learned it from friends in Detroit.

Widziałem Marysie raz we młynie,
Widziałem Marysie raz we młynie,
Jak lazła na góre po drabinie,
Jak lazła na góre po drabinie.

Troszeczkę było jej widać nogi;
Takuchne jak sosny, Boże drogi.

I once saw fair Mary in the grist mill,
I once saw fair Mary in the grist mill,
As upward and up the ladder she climbed,
As upward and up the ladder she climbed.

'Twas then that I saw a bit of her legs.
Like pines, strong and sturdy they were, dear
[God.

Tak żem się zakochał w niej szalenie
Że niczem mi picie, ni jedzenie.

Zachodzę raz do niej i się pytam
Czy chciała się zostać mą kobietą.

A ona mi na to, "Chuderlaku,
Weź sznurek i powieś się na krzaku.

"Bo ja chcę mieć męża morowego,
A ty za pół roku do niczego."

I dostała męża jak niedźwiedzia;
W pół roku podobny był do śledzia.

Dobrze żem nie jej mąż, myślę sobie,
Bo dawno bym był już leżał w grobie.

Ona płacze, narzeka; ja jej na to
"A widzisz, dobrze ci, ty harmato."

So madly I fell in love with this girl,
All food and all drink were nothing to me.

One day when I called, I wanted to know
If she would consent to be my woman.

But she answered me, "You skinny bean pole,
Go fetch some old rope and hang from that bush.

"My husband must be both sturdy and strong;
But you'll be worth nought in six months or so."

And so she did wed a bear-like strong man,
Alas, in six months, a weak fish was he.

What luck, I now thought, that I'm not her man,
Or long before this I would have been dead.

When she cries and complains, I now tell her,
"Now see here, old cannon ball, serves you right."

56
Niema-ci To, Nie Ma
NOTHING, REALLY NOTHING

Giocoso

Nie-ma - ci to, nie ma Jak mu - lar - ska
Noth-ing, real-ly noth-ing Beats the ma-son's

mi - na. Za - ro - bi szóz ta - ka, To pa - li wer-
for-tune. With his pret-ty earn-ings He smokes a Vir-

dzi - na. Hej! wi - niu, wi - niu, Hej! wi - niu,
gin-ia. Hey! vee-niu, vee-niu, Hey! vee-niu,

wi - niu, Hej! wi - niu, wi - niu, mój!
vee-niu, Hey! vee-niu, vee-niu, mine!

Sung in 1941 by Frank First, who learned it from his father-in-law,
who came from Krosno, Poland.

Niema-ci to, nie ma
Jak mularska mina.
Zarobi szóstaka,
To pali werdzina.

Nothing, really nothing
Beats the mason's fortune.
With his pretty earnings
He smokes a Virginia.

Hej! winiu, winiu,
Hej! winiu, winiu,
Hej! winiu, winiu mój!

"Za murarza pójdę;
Będę masło jadła,
Dwa garnce kartofli,
A za centa sadła.

"Za murarza pójdę;
Nie będę robiła.
Kupi mi sukienkę;
Będę się cieszyła.

"Za murarza pójdę;
Będę wielką panią.
Sprawi mi sukmanę;
Będzie się wlec za mną."

"Za murarza poszła,
I robić musiała.
Jak robić nie chciała,
Po karku dostała.

Idzie murarz miedzą
I tak wygwizduje.
A wsza po kołnierzu
Kadryła tańcuje.

Refrain:
Hey! veeniu, veeniu,
Hey! veeniu, veeniu,
Hey! veeniu, veeniu mine!

"I will wed a mason;
I'll have butter daily,
Of potatoes plenty
Penny's worth of bacon.

"I will wed a mason;
I shall be a lady.
A fine frock he'll buy me;
That will make me happy.

"I will wed a mason;
I'll be a grand lady.
He'll buy me a mantle
That will trail behind me."

A mason she married;
Work she had a-plenty.
When she missed her duties,
Blows rained on her poor head.

A mason was walking
Through the meadow, whistling.
A flea danced a quadrille
Right upon his collar.

57
Nędzne Życie Czeladnika[23]
WOEFUL IS THE HIRED MAN'S FORTUNE

Moderato

Nędz - ne ży - cie cze - lad - ni - ka.
Woe - ful is the hired man's for - tune.

Na śnia - da - nie szklan - kę mle - ka,
For his break - fast, one glass of milk,

I o - bia - dek ja - ki ta - ki. Nędz - ne
And his din - ner, it's just so - so. Woe - ful

ży - cie cze - lad - ni - ka. Dzi - siaj w świe - cie ta - ki
is the hired man's for - tune. The world's run like this to -

stan: Kto pie - nią - dze ma ten pan.
day: He who's mon - ey'd is top man.

Sung in 1941 by Mrs. Sophia Dziob, who learned it from her husband,
who had learned it in Nowy Sącz, Poland.

Nędzne życie czeladnika.
Na śniadanie szklankę mleka,
I obiadek jaki taki.
Nędzne życie czeladnika.

Refren:
Dzisiaj w świecie taki stan:
Kto pieniądze ma ten pan.

Dzisiaj panny nic nie dbają,
Za pieniądze serce dają.
Śliczne, piękne, uczone,
Za pieniądze są kupione.

Żeby ja miał cztery reńskie,
Kochał bym ja panny miejskie.
Lecz ja nie mam ni szeląga;
Muszę kochać ze wsi drąga.

*Woeful is the hired man's fortune.
For his breakfast, one glass of milk,
And his dinner, it's just so-so.
Woeful is the hired man's fortune.*

Refrain:
*The world's run like this today:
He who's money'd is top man.*

*Girls today are so indifferent,
Hearts they'll give away for money.
Beauties, lovelies, learnèd maids,
May be purchased for your money.*

*Would my savings were four florins,
I could love the city maidens.
But I have not e'en a farthing;
I must love some village hoyden.*

58

Jedzie Wóz Po Pod Wóz

WAGONS COME ROLLING BY

(See number 59)

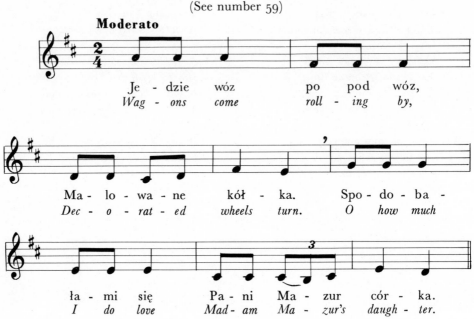

Moderato

Je - dzie wóz po pod wóz,
Wag - ons come roll - ing by,

Ma - lo - wa - ne kół - ka. Spo - do - ba -
Dec - o - rat - ed wheels turn. O how much

ła - mi się Pa - ni Ma - zur cór - ka.
I do love Mad - am Ma - zur's daugh - ter.

Sung in 1940 by Mrs. Alexandra Szczepanik, who learned it from her
father in Poland when she was a child.

Jedzie wóz po pod wóz,	*Wagons come rolling by,*
Malowane kólka.	*Decorated wheels turn.*
Spodobała mi się	*O how much I do love*
Pani Mazur córka.	*Madam Mazur's daughter.*
Będę listy pisał	*I shall write notes of love,*
Będę je malował,	*I shall decorate them,*
Aby mi Pan Mazur	*So that Mister Mazur*
Córkę podarował.	*Will let me have his daughter.*
Nie dla psa kiełbasa,	*Not for dogs is sausage,*
Nie dla kotka szpyrka;	*Nor do cats eat bacon.*
Nie dla ciebie, durniu	*Just forget, you blockhead,*
Mazurowa córka.	*Madam Mazur's daughter.*

59
Nie Dla Psa Kiełbasa
NOT FOR DOGS IS SAUSAGE
(Variant of number 58)

Nie dla psa kieł - ba - sa, Nie dla
Not for dogs is sau - sage, Nor do

kot - ka szpyr - ka. Nie dla cie - bie Ja - siu,
cats get ba - con. Just for - get, dear John - ny,

Las - kow - skie - go cór - ka. Oj da - na.
Las - kow - ski's fair daugh - ter. O da - na.

Sung in 1941 by Mrs. John Krupski, who learned it from her mother
in Buffalo.

Nie dla psa kiełbasa,
Nie dla kotka szpyrka.
Nie dla ciebie Jasiu,
Laskowskiego córka.
Oj dana!

Not for dogs is sausage,
Nor do cats get bacon.
Just forget, dear Johnny,
Laskowski's fair daughter.
O dana!

60

A Wy Juchy, Wy Mazury

O YOU SCOUNDRELS, YOU MAZOVIANS

A wy ju - chy, wy Ma - zu - ry,
O you scoun - drels, you Ma - zo - vians,

Wy Ma - zu - ry, U - kra - dliś - cie skó - ry z gó - ry,
You Ma - zo - vians, You stole leath - er from my at - tic,

Skó - ry z gó - ry. Dar - mo się chwa - li - cie;
From my at - tic. Vain - ly do you swag - ger;

Od - dać je mu - si - cie. Dar - mo się
You must now re - turn it. Vain - ly do

chwa - li - cie; Od - dać je mu - si - cie.
you swag - ger; You must now re - turn it.

Sung in 1940 by Mrs. Helen Poplawska, who learned it from the
children in Narol, Poland.

A wy juchy, wy Mazury,
Wy Mazury,
Ukradliście skóry z góry,
Skóry z góry.
Darmo się chwalicie;
Oddać je musicie.
Darmo się chwalicie;
Oddać je musicie.

Mam trzewiki z dobrej skóry,
Z dobrej skóry,
Co mi robił szewczyk z góry,
Szewczyk z góry.
Podkóweczki szklące
Za cztery tysiące.

O you scoundrels, you Mazovians,
You Mazovians,
You stole leather from my attic,
From my attic.
Vainly do you swagger;
You must now return it.
Vainly do you swagger;
You must now return it.

I have shoes of finest leather,
Finest leather.
They were made by yonder cobbler,
Yonder cobbler.
Heels of sparkling lustre
Worth at least four thousand.

61

Tyleż-ty, Tyle Ty[24]

HAPLESS, O HOW HAPLESS

Energico

Ty - leż - ty,   ty - le ty   Mo - jej
Hap - less,   O   how   hap - less   My   ill -

u - cie - chy;   Cho - dzi - łam   do   la - su
starred   heart   is;   Vain - ly   did   I   gath - er

Zbie - ra - łam   o - rze - chy.   Dla   Ja - sien - ka
Nuts   in   the   green   for - est   For   my   John - ny,

mi - łe - go,   Dla   Ja - sien - ka   mi - łe - go.
my   dear   love,   For   my   John - ny,   my   dear   love.

Sung in 1940 by Mrs. Sophia Dziob, who learned it in Tomaszowce, Poland.

Tyleż-ty, tyle ty	*Hapless, O how hapless*
Mojej uciechy;	*My ill-starred heart is;*
Chodziłam do lasu	*Vainly did I gather*
Zbierałam orzechy.	*Nuts in the green forest*
Dla Jasieńka miłego,	*For my Johnny, my dear love,*
Dla Jasieńka miłego.	*For my Johnny, my dear love.*

Poszłam do karczmiska,
Usiadłam na progu;
Mój miły tańcuje,
Chwała-ć Panu Bogu.
Chusteczką się ociera
I do tańca wybiera.

Poszedł przed muzykant,
Rzucił talarami.
Ja biedna sierota,
Zalałam się łzami.
I z tego frasoneczku,
Poszłam spać do domeczku.

Poszłam do domeczku,
Siadłam na łóżeczku,
I tak sobie myślę
O swem kochaneczku.
A on idzie i puka,
"Otwórz Hańciu, bo to ja."

"Nie będę wstawała,
Ani otwierała,
Bo bym już tych nocek
Nie narachowała
Coś się do mnie nachodził
I mnie biedną nazwodził."

A on ci ją prosi,
A on ci ją łaje.
Jedwabną chusteczkę
A on ci jej daje.
"Ja chusteczki nie chcę brać.
Ciebie durniu nie chcę znać."

"Moja najmilejsza,
Zechciej wyrozumieć,
Bo jak chcesz tańcować,
Musisz dobrze umieć.
Bo ja nierad tańcuję
Jak mam marną tańcule."

I went to the tavern,
Sat upon the doorstep;
I watched Johnny dancing,
Praise be God Almighty.
And he mopped his forehead moist,
Then began another dance.

Standing near the fiddlers,
He tossed dollars to them,
Wretched girl that I am,
Blinding tears o'erwhelmed me.
After this embarrassment,
I went home and off to bed.

I went to my cottage,
On my bed I pondered;
And thus I reflected
On my faithless lover.
When he tapped upon the pane,
"Open Annie; it is I."

"I'll not get up for you,
I'll not let you in.
Nights we've spent together
Are too great to number,
When you came to call on me,
Only to delude my heart."

He begged her and pleaded;
He chided and scolded.
And a silken kerchief
He e'en offered to her.
"You can keep your silk kerchief.
I don't want to know you, churl."

"Look here, my sweet darling,
Try to understand me.
If you would go dancing,
You should not be clumsy.
For I do not like to dance
With a heavy-footed girl."

III

Singers are weavers of ballads, tales of infinite variety and enduring sameness.[25]

62

Czarna Rola Biały Kamień[1]

FERTILE BLACK SOIL AND WHITE FIELD STONE

(Variant of numbers 2 and 63)

Czar - na ro - la, bia - ły ka - mień,
Fer - tile black soil and white field stone,

Czar - na ro - la, bia - ły ka - mień.
Fer - tile black soil and white field stone,

Po - do - lan - ka sie - dzi na nim,
A Po - do - lienne sits up - on it,

Po - do - lan - ka sie - dzi na nim.
A Po - do - lienne sits up - on it.

Sung in 1941 by Mrs. John Krupski, who learned it from friends
in Buffalo.

Czarna rola, biały kamień,   *Fertile black soil and white field stone,*
Czarna rola, biały kamień.   *Fertile black soil and white field stone.*
Podolanka siedzi na nim,   *A Podolienne sits upon it,*
Podolanka siedzi na nim.   *A Podolienne sits upon it.*

Przyszedł do niej Podoleniec,   *A Podolian youth came to her.*
"Podolanko, daj mi wieniec."   *"I would have your wreath, fair maiden."*

"Rada bym ci wieniec dała,
Bym się brata nie bojała."

"Otruj, otruj brata swego;
Będziesz miała mnie samego."

"O Boże, mi grzechy odpuść,
Bym wiedziała czem go otruć."

"Idź do gaju zielonego;
Ukój węża trującego.

"Ugotuj go w czarnej jusze,
Nim zatracisz brata dusze.

"Ugotuj go mięciusieńko,
Posiekaj go drobniusieńko.

"I przelej go do szklanicy,
I zanieś go do piwnicy.

"Gdy przyjedzie brat spragniony
Będzie wołał szklankę wody.

"Wtenczas ty idź do piwnicy
I przynieś mu we szklanicy."

A brat wypił i zawołał,
"Siostro, siostro, otrułaś mnie."

"Mój braciszku, upiłeś się;
Weź poduszki, prześpij-że się."

Tęgie to tam zasypianie,
Ciało z duszą rozłączanie.

". . . . .
Już otrułam brata mego."

"Otrułaś ty brata swego,
Otruła byś mnie samego."

Braciszkowi dzwony dzwonią;
A siostrzyczkę diabły gonią.

Braciszkowi wyśpiewują;
A siostrzyczkę diabły kują.

"*Gladly would I give it to you,
If I did not fear my brother.*"

"*Feed your brother poison, poison;
There will be no one between us.*"

"*God forgive me my transgressions.
Would I knew which poison to give.*"

"*Go into the forest glade;
Kill a snake of deadly venom.*

"*Boil it in its foul dark gore,
Ere you lose your brother's soul.*

"*Boil it 'til it's soft and tender;
Chop it finely; mince it well.*

"*Then into a tumbler pour it,
And down to the cellar take it.*

"*When your brother comes a-thirsting,
He will want a glass of water.*

"*You will go down to the cellar;
Fetch it for him in a tumbler.*"

*So he drank and then he called out,
"Sister, Sister, you have poisoned me.*"

"*My dear brother, you are drunken.
Take these pillows; you need slumber.*"

*Heavy is the slumber, indeed,
That can wrest the soul from body.*

"*. . . . .
Poisoned have I now my brother.*"

"*If you've poisoned your own brother,
No doubt you would poison me, too.*"

*Bells are tolling for the brother;
Devils chase the evil sister.*

*Hymns are sung for the poor brother,
While the devils chain the sister.*

63

Na Podolu Biały Kamień[1]

LO! A WHITE ROCK IN PODOLIA

(Variant of numbers 2 and 62)

Allegretto

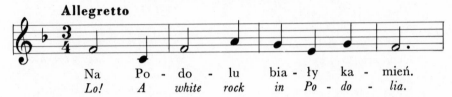

Na Po - do - lu bia - ły ka - mień.
Lo! A white rock in Po - do - lia.

Po - do - lan - ka, dy - ja - kom ta - kom,
A Po - do - lienne, tra - la - la - la - la,

Dy - ja - kom ta - kom, sie - dzi na nim.
Tra - la - la - la - la, sits up - on it.

Sung in 1941 by Frank First, who learned it from his sister,
who had learned it in Sonina, Poland.

Na Podolu biały kamień.
Podolanka, dyjakom takom,
Dyjakom takom, siedzi na nim.
Podolanka, dyjakom takom,
Dyjakom takom, siedzi na nim.

Lo! A white rock in Podolia.
A Podolienne, tra la la la la,
Tra la la la la, sits upon it.
A Podolienne, tra la la la la,
Tra la la la la, sits upon it.

Siedzi, siedzi, wieniec wije.
Siedzi, siedzi, dyjakom takom,
Dyjakom takom, wieniec wije.

There she sits and weaves a fine wreath.
There she sits, tra la la la la,
Tra la la la la, weaves a fine wreath.

Jeden z róż, dwa z liliji.
Jeden z róż, dyjakom takom,
Dyjakom takom, dwa z liliji.

One of roses, two of lilies,
One of roses, tra la la la la,
Tra la la la la, two of lilies.

Przyszedł do niej cudzoziemiec.
Przyszedł do niej, dyjakom takom,
Dyjakom takom, cudzoziemiec.

"Podolanko, daj mi wieniec.
Podolanko, dyjakom takom,
Dyjakom takom, daj mi wieniec."

"Nie dam ja ci wieńca tego.
Nie dam ja ci, dyjakom takom
Dyjakom takom, wieńca tego.

"Bo się boję męża swego.
Bo się boję, dyjakom takom,
Dyjakom takom, męża swego."

Once a stranger came to see her,
Once a stranger, tra la la la la,
Tra la la la la, came to see her.

"Maid of Podolia, give me your wreath.
Maid of Podolia, tra la la la la,
Tra la la la la, give me your wreath."

"I cannot give this wreath to you,
I cannot give, tra la la la la,
Tra la la la la, this wreath to you.

"For I greatly fear my husband,
For I greatly, tra la la la la,
Tra la la la la, fear my husband."

64

Tam Poza Góry[26]

FROM BEYOND THE HILLS

Gaily

Tam po-za gó - ry Ja - dą Ma - zu - ry. Tam po-
From be-yond the hills Ride the Ma - zo - vians. From be-

rit.

za gó - ry Ja - dą Ma - zu - ry. Je - dzie, je - dzie
yond the hills Ride the Ma - zo - vians. And my love comes

Ko - cha - ne - czek, Wie - zie, wie - zie Mój wia - ne - czek,
rid - ing, rid - ing, Bring - ing me my Gar - land, gar - land,

1

Pięk - ny ró - żo - wy, Pięk - ny ró - żo - wy.
Pink and beau - ti - ful, Pink and beau - ti - ful.

6 *rit.*

Pięk - ny ró - żo - wy, Pięk - ny ró - żo - wy.
Pink and beau - ti - ful, Pink and beau - ti - ful.

Sung in 1940 by Harriet Pawlowska, who learned it from her father,
who had learned it in Kaiew, Poland.

"Tam poza góry
Jadą Mazury.
Tam poza góry
Jadą Mazury.
Jedzie, jedzie
Kochaneczek,
Wiezie, wiezie
Mój wianeczek,
Piękny różowy,
Piękny różowy.

"Przyjechał w nocy
Przed moje oczy.
Przyjechał w nocy
Przed moje oczy.
Sztuk, puk
W okieneczko;"
"Wstań, wstań,
Panieneczko;
Daj koniom wody;
Daj koniom wody."

"Jakże ja mam wstać
Koniom wody dać?
Jakże ja mam wstać
Koniom wody dać?
Zimna rosa
A ja bosa;
Zimna rosa
A ja bosa.
Nie mogę wytrwać;
Nie mogę wytrwać."

"Na masz chusteczki;
Owiń nóżeczki.
Na masz chusteczki;
Owiń nóżeczki.
Gdy mi miły
Bóg wspomoże,
Gdy mi miły
Bóg wspomoże,
Kupię trzewiczki,
Kupię trzewiczki."

*"From beyond the hills
Ride the Mazovians.
From beyond the hills
Ride the Mazovians.
And my love comes
Riding, riding,
Bringing me my
Garland, garland,
Pink and beautiful,
Pink and beautiful.*

*"He arrived at night
Right before my eyes.
He arrived at night
Right before my eyes.
Tap, tap, tap, tap,
At my window;"
"Rise now, rise now,
My dear sweetheart;
Will you feed my horse?
Will you feed my horse?"*

*"How can I get up
Your fine horse to feed?
How can I get up
Your fine horse to feed?
Cold is the dew,
Bare are my feet;
Cold is the dew,
Bare are my feet;
That I can't endure,
That I can't endure."*

*"Take my handkerchief;
Wrap your little feet.
Take my handkerchief;
Wrap your little feet.
And when I am
Blest with God's help,
And when I am
Blest with God's help,
I shall buy you shoes,
I shall buy you shoes."*

127

"Kupisz nie kupisz,
Ja będę miała.
Kupisz nie kupisz,
Ja będę miała.
Bo mi mama
Przykazała
Żebym z tobą
Nie mawiała;
Muszę ją słuchać.
Muszę ją słuchać.

"Mamy nie słuchaj;
Siadaj na mój koń.
Mamy nie słuchaj;
Siadaj na mój koń.
Pojedziemy
W obce kraje
Gdzie są inne
Obyczaje.
Malowany dwór.
Malowany dwór."

"*You buy them or no,
I shall have my shoes.
You buy them or no,
I shall have my shoes.
For my mamma
Strictly told me
Not to talk with
You, my dear one.
Her I must obey,
Her I must obey.*"

"*Do not heed Mamma;
Get upon my horse.
Do not heed Mamma;
Get upon my horse.
We shall ride to
Foreign countries,
Where the customs
Widely differ;
Castles in the air,
Castles in the air.*"

65

Jasio Konie Poił[27]

JOHN WAS WAT'RING HORSES

(See number 66)

Ja - sio ko - nie po - ił, Ka - sia
John was wa - t'ring hors - es, Kate was

wo - dę bra - ła. Co Ja - sio za -
draw - ing wa - ter. John - ny's heart sang

śpie - wał, Ka - sia za - pła - ka - ła.
gai - ly, Kate was far from hap - py.

Sung in 1940 by Mrs. Sophia Dziob, who learned it in the village
of Tomaszowce, Poland.

Jasio konie poił,
Kasia wodę brała.
Co Jasio zaśpiewał,
Kasia zapłakała.

"Czemu Kasiu płaczesz?
Czemu lamentujesz?
Gdzie ty zechcesz Kasiu,
Ze mną powędrujesz."

Wędrowała bym-ja,
Czemu bym nie miała,
Żeby mi mamusia
Strojów nie chowała."

John was wat'ring horses,
Kate was drawing water.
Johnny's heart sang gaily,
Kate was far from happy.

"Katie, why the tears, dear?
Why the lamentation?
Choose the road, dear Katie,
I will take you with me."

"Gladly would I travel,
Nought would stop me, Johnny,
If my mamma had not
Locked up all my finery."

"Jak ci główka boli
To powiedz matuli,
A ona cię wpuści
Do nowej komory."

*"Why not tell your mother
That you have a headache?
Then, indeed, she'll let you
Rest inside the new room."*

Mamusia myślała
Że Kasia choruje,
A Kasia z Jasieńkiem
Całą noc wędruje.

*And so Katie's mamma
Thought that she was ailing,
But her Kate was traveling
All night long with Johnny.*

I przywędrowali
Do ciemnego lasu.
"Rozpuszczaj Kasieńko
Warkoczyk zawczasu."

*And at last they wandered
To a forest dreary.
"Loosen here, my Katie,
Your fair braids in good time."*

"Nie na to mi mama
Czesała i pletła,
Żebym ja po krzakach
Swój warkoczyk wlekła."

*"Not for this did Mamma
Comb and plait my tresses,
Now to drag and snarl them
Over all these brambles."*

I przywędrowali
Na ten most szeroki.
Rzucił Jasio Kasię
Na Dunaj głęboki.

*When at last they wandered
To that long and wide bridge,
Johnny threw poor Katie
Deep into the Danube.*

"Gruntuj-że mi gruntuj,
Warkoczyku do dna,
Bo ja od Jasieńka
Tej śmierci nie godna."

*"Anchor me, O fair braids,
To the water's bottom.
Undeserving am I
Of such a fate from Johnny."*

Byli tam rybacy
Co ryby łowili,
Nadobną Kasieńkę
Na brzeg wyrzucili.

*Fishermen were nearby
Dragging in their fish,
And they dragged fair Katie
From the watery bottom.*

I posadzili ją
Na białem kamieniu,
Rozpuścili włosy
Po prawem ramieniu.

*And they placed her gently
On a glistening white rock,
And they spread her tresses[28]
Over her right shoulder.*

A był tam braciszek
Na wysokiej górze,
Spuścił się do Kasi
Po jedwabnem sznurze.

*High upon a mountain
Katie's brother saw this;
Down he slid to Katie
On a silken cable.*

"Nie tak mi cię szkoda
Ale twego wianka,
Boś se ulubiła
Łajdaka kochanka."

Niebodze Kasieńce
W cztery dzwony dzwonią,
A Jasia hultaja
W cztery konie gonią.

Niebogę Kasieńkę
Do grobu wkładają,
A Jasia hultaja
Na sznurze wieszają.

*"Less I grieve for you, Kate,
Then for your lost garland.
You have loved unwisely
A roué, my poor girl."*

*Poor dear wretched Katie,
Four bells toll her sad fate.
But that villain, Johnny!
Horses four pursue him.*

*Poor dear wretched Katie
To her grave is lowered.
But that villain, Johnny!
From a rope he dangles.*

66

Jaś Konika Poił [27]

WHILE JOHNNY FED HIS HORSE

(Variant of number 65)

Jaś ko - ni - ka po - ił, Ka - sia wo - dę bra -
While John - ny fed his horse, Ka - tie was draw - ing

ła. _____ Jaś Ka - się na - ma - wiał, Jaś Ka - się
wa - ter. John - ny was urg - ing Kate, John - ny was

na - ma - wiał Że - by węd - ro - wa - ła. _____ ła. _____
urg - ing Kate To wan - der off with him. _____ him. _____

Sung in 1941 by Frank First, who learned it from his sister,
who had learned it in Sonina, Poland.

Jaś konika poił,	*While Johnny fed his horse,*
Kasia wodę brała.	*Katie was drawing water.*
Jaś Kasię namawiał,	*Johnny was urging Kate,*
Jaś Kasię namawiał	*Johnny was urging Kate*
Żeby wędrowała.	*To wander off with him.*
Jaś Kasię namawiał,	*Johnny was urging Kate,*
Jaś Kasię namawiał	*Johnny was urging Kate*
Żeby wędrowała.	*To wander off with him.*
"Powiedz że mamusi	*"Why not tell your mother*
Że ci głowa boli,	*Your head is sore with pain?*
To ci mama odda	*You will then get the keys*
Klucze od komory."	*To the padlocked storeroom."*

Mamusia myślała	And so her mamma thought
Że Kasieńka spała,	Katie was resting there,
A Kasia z Jasieńkiem	But Kate was wandering
W świat powędrowała.	Over the world with John.
Nie daleko uszli,	They had not gone too far,
Tylko kawałeczek,	Just a short way from home.
"Wroćmy się Kasieńko	"Katie, let us return
Na ten twój domeczek."	Home to your cottage now."
"Nie na tom jechała	"I have not wandered forth
Żebym się wracała,	Only to go back now,
Żebym ojcu, matcę	Only to bring sorrow
Żalu dodawała."	To my dear father, mother."
I wziął ją za rączkę	He seized her tiny hand,
I wziął ją pod boczek,	He caught her 'round the waist,
I rzucił ją, rzucił	He threw her, he threw her
W Dunajec głęboki.	Into the deep Danube.
Tylko się wianeczek	And lo! her pretty wreath
Zawiesił na kole.	Was caught around a pole.
"Ratuj mnie, Jasieńku,	"Save me, my dear Johnny,
Ratuj, serce moje."	Save me, my heart of hearts."
"Nie na tom cię rzucał	"I did not cast you off
Żebym cię ratował,	Only to save you now,
Żebym ci wianeczek	Only to untangle
Z kołeczka zdejmował."	Your garland from the pole."
Siciarze, rybiarze,	Netweavers, fishermen,
Sicie zakładajcie.	Make your nets ready, now.
Nadobną Kasieńkę	And beautiful Katie
Z wody wyciągajcie.	Drag from the water, now.

67

Cztery Mile Za Warszawą

IT WAS FOUR MILES OUT OF WARSAW

Czte - ry mi - le za War - sza - wą,
It was four miles out of War - saw,

Czte - ry mi - le za War - sza - wą
It was four miles out of War - saw

Star - sza sios - tra wy - szła za mąż,
That an el - der sis - ter mar - ried,

Star - sza sios - tra wy - szła za mąż.
That an el - der sis - ter mar - ried.

Sung in 1941 by Frank First, who had learned it from his wife.
She had learned it from a member of her family in Krosno, near Kraków.

Cztery mile za Warszawą,
Cztery mile za Warszawą
Starsza siostra wyszła za mąż,
Starsza siostra wyszła za mąż.

Wyszła za mąż za zbójnika,
Za starszego rozpustnika.

It was four miles out of Warsaw,
It was four miles out of Warsaw
That an elder sister married,
That an elder sister married.

She was married to an outlaw,
An old bandit wise in his ways.

Co po nocy wciąż polował,
Nigdy w domu nie nocował.

"Raz mi przyniósł chustkę białą
Całą we krwi ówalaną."

"Żono moja wypierz mi ją
I na słońcu wysusz mi ją."

Ona prała i płakała
Bo chusteczkę poznawała.

"Ta chusteczka brata mego
Wczoraj wieczór zabitego."

"Nie płacz, żono, nie rozgłaszaj.
Ciemno było, deszczyk rosił.
Jam nie zważał, on się prosił,
Jam nie zważał, on się prosił."

O how oft he roamed the whole night,
Seldom did he stay at home nights.

"Once a handkerchief he brought me
That with human blood was covered."

"My dear wife, now wash it for me.
In the sun do bleach it for me."

So she washed it and grieved deeply,
For the handkerchief she knew well.

"'Tis my brother's; well I know it.
He was murdered well past midnight."

"Do not cry, wife; keep my secret.
It was dark, the rain was falling.
Nought I cared, although he pleaded,
Nought I cared, although he pleaded."

68

Tam Za Krakowem Na Błoniu[29]
'WAY BEYOND KRAKOW IN THE MEAD

Moderato

Tam za Kra - ko - wem na bło - niu,
'Way be - yond Kra - kow in the mead,

Tam za Kra - ko - wem, a lu lu, A lu lu,
'Way be - yond Kra - kow, a lu lu, A lu lu,

lu lu lu, Wy - jeż - dzał Ja - sio na ko - niu.
lu lu lu, John - ny rode forth up - on his horse.

A lullaby, sung in 1941 by Frank First, who learned it from his sister after she came to the United States from Sonina, Poland.

Tam za Krakowem na błoniu,
Tam za Krakowem, a lu lu,
A lu lu, lu lu lu,
Wyjeżdzał Jasio na koniu.

Kasia Jasiowa chodziła,
Kasia Jasiowa, a lu lu,
A lu lu, lu lu lu,
Małe dzieciątko nosiła.

"Rzuć Kasiu dziecię do wody,
Rzuć Kasiu dziecię, a lu lu,
A lu lu, lu lu lu,
Nie będziesz miała przeszkody."

'Way beyond Krakow in the mead,
'Way beyond Krakow, a lu lu,
A lu lu, lu lu lu,
Johnny rode forth upon his horse.

Kate followed Johnny here and there,
Kate followed Johnny, a lu lu,
A lu lu, lu lu lu,
A tiny infant in her arms.

"Kate, throw the babe into the sea;
Kate, throw the babe, a lu lu,
A lu lu, lu lu lu,
Then you will have no obstacle."

Kasia swe dziecię rzuciła,
Kasia swe dziecię, a lu lu,
A lu lu, lu lu lu,
Sama się we świat puściła.

Siedział tam rybak na lądzie
Siedział tam rybak, a lu lu
A lu lu, lu lu lu,
Złapał te dziecię na wodzie.

Wszystkie panienki na mieście,
Wszystkie panienki, a lu lu,
A lu lu, lu lu lu,
Kasia Jasiowa w areszcie.

"A zróbcie ze mną co chcecie,
A zróbcie ze mną, a lu lu,
A lu lu, lu lu lu,
Niech się nie męczę na świecie."

Kate threw the babe into the sea;
Kate threw the babe, a lu lu,
A lu lu, lu lu lu,
Then she went forth into the world.

A fisherman sat upon the bank,
A fisherman sat, a lu lu,
A lu lu, lu lu lu,
He pulled the baby to the land.

All the young maids have come to town,
All the young maids, a lu lu,
A lu lu, lu lu lu,
To see John's Katie arrested.

"O do with me whatever you will,
Do with me whate'er, a lu lu,
A lu lu, lu lu lu,
But end my suffering in this world."

69

Zeszła Gwiazdka Nad Kośćółkiem [30]

RISING STAR, SHINE O'ER THE STEEPLE

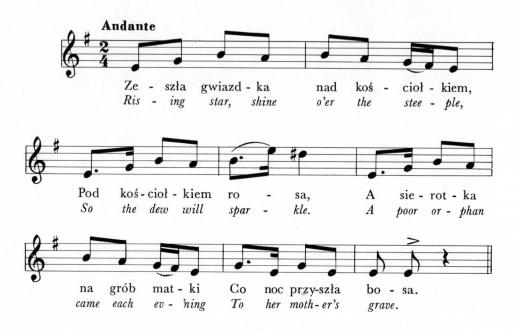

Sung by Mrs. John Krupski, who learned it from her friends in Buffalo.

Zeszła gwiazdka nad kośćółkiem,	*Rising star, shine o'er the steeple,*
Pod kośćółkiem rosa,	*So the dew will sparkle.*
A sierotka na grób matki	*A poor orphan came each ev'ning*
Co noc przyszła bosa.	*To her mother's grave.*
Na kalinach śpiące ptaszki	*With her weeping she awakened*
Kwileniem budziła.	*Birds upon the white rose.*
Tłukła główkę, włosy rwała,	*Tearing her hair, beating her head,*
Długo nie pożyła.	*She, too, died before long.*
Między błuszczem i barwikem,	*Mid the ivy, periwinkle,*
Ostem i pokrzywą,	*Thistles and the nettles,*
Kopacz znalazł na tym grobie	*A gravedigger found the body*
Sierotkę nie żywą.	*Of the bereaved orphan.*

Po trzech dniach ją pochowali
W dołku pod kościołem.
Ale szkoda, pochowali
Nie przy matce społem.

Grób matczyny przy kośćółku
Był po stronie jednej,
A po drugiej za kośćołkiem
Grób sierotki biednej.

Tam na grobie, na matczynym,
Lipka wyrastała,
A sierotce zkądziś brzóźka
Sama się zasiała.

I choć matka ze sierotką
Nie leżały społem,
Wszelako się lipka z brzózką
Zrosły nad kościołem.

Three days later she was buried
In a churchyard hollow.
But alas, she was not buried
Alongside her mother.

Along one side of the small church
They buried her mother.
And they laid the orphan to rest
On the other side.

Lo, on that grave, on the mother's,
Sprang a little lime tree.
And somehow, upon the orphan's,
A birch tree was seeded.

Though the mother and the daughter
Did not lie together,
High above the church, the branches
Of the two trees joined hands.[31]

70

W Pogodny Wieczór

MID TWILIGHT SHADOWS

(See numbers 71 and 72)

Andante

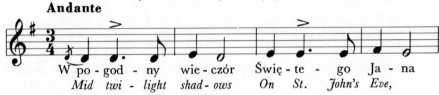

W po-god-ny wie-czór Świę-te-go Ja-na
Mid twi-light shad-ows On St. John's Eve,

Ci-chy pa-gó-rek z wie-czo-ra; A przy pa-
Ev-'ning peace falls o'er the val-ley; And in this

gór-ku Sie-dzia-ła ma-ma, Trzy-ma-ła cór-kę zem-
val-ley, A sad moth-er sits, Try-ing to con-sole her

dlo-ną. A przy pa-gór-ku Sie-dzia-ła
daugh-ter. And in this val-ley, A sad moth-

ma-ma Trzy-ma-ła cór-kę zem-dlo-ną.
er sits, Try-ing to con-sole her daugh-ter.

Sung in 1940 by Harriet Pawlowska, who learned it from her father.
He learned it in Kaiew, Poland.

W pogodny wieczór
Św. Jana
Cichy pagórek z wieczora;
A przy pagórku
Siedziała mama,
Trzymała córkę zemdloną.
A przy pagórku
Siedziała mama,
Trzymała córkę zemdloną.

"Nie płacz Karolciu,
Nie płacz aniele,
Nie jeden Oleś na świecie.
Chociaż on u nas
Nie bywał wiele
Ale jak wróci, nie rzuci."

"Ach mamo droga,
On już nie wróci
Bo moje serce tak bije.
Może go w drodze
Koń z siodła zrzuci,
Albo zły człowiek zabije."

Oleś powraca,
Już jest po ślubie;
Weselni goście się bawią.
A Karolina
Na innym łonie,
Inny jej usta całuje.

"Ach Karolino,
Gdzie są twe słowa
I wszystkie twoje zaklęcia?
Tyś mi mówiła
'Powróć a powróć',
A teraz z innym ślub wzięłaś.

"O koniu, koniu,
Wracaj do domu,
Nie ma tu siana dla ciebie.
Tam przy dolinie
Gdzie strumyk płynie,
Tam nasza pościel posłana."

Mid twilight shadows
On St. John's Eve,[32]
Ev'ning peace falls o'er the valley;
And in this valley,
A sad mother sits,
Trying to console her daughter.
And in this valley,
A sad mother sits,
Trying to console her daughter.

"Weep not, my Carol,
Weep not, my angel,
O there is more than one Alex.
Though he has seldom
Been here, my darling,
When he returns, he will see you."

"O dearest Mother,
I'll never see him;
My fast beating heart tells me so.
While on his journey
His horse may throw him,
Or an evil man may kill him."

Alex returns
After the marriage;
Wedding guests are rejoicing.
He sees another
Kissing his loved one,
Kissing the lips which she offers.

"O faithless Carol,
Where is your promise?
Where is the oath that you made me?
You warmly begged me,
'Return O return,'
And now you have wed another.

"O faithful steed,
Let us turn homeward;
There is no hay for you here.
In yonder valley,
Where flows the river,
There our bed is made and waiting."

Koniczek skręcił,
Aż z pod kopyta
Czerwona iskra wyprysła.
Młodzieniec jęknął,
Szabla zabłysła,
Zginął jak polska korona.

The horse turned smartly,
And from his fleet hoof
Fiery red sparks flashed brightly.
The youth in anguish,
Felled by his own sword,
Was lost like the crown of Poland.

71

W Pogodny Wieczór

MID TWILIGHT SHADOWS

(Variant of numbers 70 and 72)

W po - god - ny wie - czór Świę - te - go Ja -
Mid twi - light shad - ows On St. John's Ev -

na. Księ - życ przy - świe - cał z pa - gór - ka.
en, Moon - light glowed o - ver the val - ley.

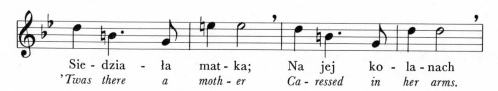

Sie - dzia - ła mat - ka; Na jej ko - la - nach
'Twas there a moth - er Ca - ressed in her arms.

Pieś - ci - ła. się lu - ba cór - ka.
A daugh - ter whom she loved dear - ly.

Sung in 1941 by Mrs. Ferdinand Chenik, who learned it from friends
in Winnepeg, Canada. This is all Mrs. Chenik could remember.

W pogodny wieczór	*Mid twilight shadows*
Sw. Jana,	*On St. John's Even,*[32]
Księżyc przyświecał z pagórka.	*Moonlight glowed over the valley.*
Siedziała matka;	*'Twas there a mother*
Na jej kolanach	*Caressed in her arms*
Pieściła się luba córka.	*A daughter whom she loved dearly.*

143

72

W Pogodny Wieczór

MID TWILIGHT SHADOWS

(Variant of numbers 70 and 71)

W po - god - ny wie - czór Świę - te - go
Mid twi - light shad - ows On St. John's

Ja - na, U stóp pięk - ne - go pa - gór - ka
Ev - en, Near yon - der beau - ti - ful hill - ock,

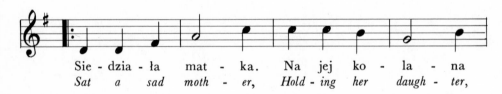

Sie - dzia - ła mat - ka. Na jej ko - la - na
Sat a sad moth - er, Hold - ing her daugh - ter,

U - pad - ła zem - dlo - na cór - ka.
Help - less and griev - ing in her arms.

Sung in 1941 by Frank First, who learned it from his mother.

W pogodny wieczór	*Mid twilight shadows*
Św. Jana,	*On St. John's Even,*[32]
U stóp pięknego pagórka	*Near yonder beautiful hillock,*
Siedziała matka.	*Sat a sad mother,*
Na jej kolana	*Holding her daughter,*
Upadła zemdlona córka.	*Helpless and grieving in her arms.*
Siedziała matka;	*Sat a sad mother,*
Na jej kolana	*Holding her daughter,*
Upadła zemdlona córka.	*Helpless and grieving in her arms.*

"O Karolino
Nie płacz aniele;
Nie jeden Leon na świecie.
Chociaż on u nas
Nie bywał wiele,
Ale nie rzuci cię przecie."

"Ach mamo, mamo,
Serce mi bije,
Że już mój Leon nie wróci.
Może go konik
Ze siodła zrzuci,
Może zły człowiek zabije."

Przyjeżdza Leon
Lecz już po ślubie,
Tylko tłum gości ucztuje.
A Karolina
Na innym łonie,
Innego usta całuje.

"O Karolino,
Tyś mnie zdradziła.
Gdziesz twoje wszystkie zaklęcia?
'Przyjedź ach przyjedź,'
Ty-żeś mówiła;
Teraż żeś w innych objęciach.

"Koniu, mój koniu,
Wróćmy do domu.
Tu dla nas nie mają siana.
Tam w tej dolinie
Gdzie strumyk płynie,
Tam nasza chata kochana."

"O Carol, darling,
Weep not my angel,
There will be others you can meet.
Though Leon seldom
Called on you, darling,
He'll ne'er forsake you, I am sure."

"O Mother, Mother,
My heart gives warning
That I will never see Leon.
While on his journey,
His horse may throw him;
He may be killed by evil men."

Leon returns
After the marriage;
Only the wedding guests greet him.
He sees another
Kissing his loved one,
Kissing the lips which she offers.

"O faithless Carol,
You have betrayed me.
Where is the oath that you made me?
Warmly you begged me,
'Come back O come back.'
Now you have found another love.

"O faithful steed,
Let us turn homeward.
We find no welcoming hearth here.
In yonder valley,
Where flows the river,
Our cottage offers warm welcome."

73

Ciemnem Borem Nad Wieczorem

THROUGH THE DARK WOOD'S EV'NING SHADOWS

Ciem - nem bo - rem nad wie - czor - em,
Through the dark wood's ev - 'ning shad - ows,

Le - ciał czar - ny kruk, I do chat - ki
Flew a ra - ven black, To a moth - er's

sta - rej mat - ki, Puk w o - kien - ko, puk!
cot - tage where he Tapped the win - dow, tap!

Sung in 1940 by Mrs. John Krupski, who learned it in Buffalo.

Ciemnem borem nad wieczorem,	*Through the dark wood's ev'ning shadows,*
Leciał czarny kruk,	*Flew a raven black,*
I do chatki starej matki,	*To a mother's cottage where he*
Puk w okienko, puk!	*Tapped the window, tap!*
"Matko moja, matko moja,	*"Mother dear, O dearest Mother,*
Przybądź co masz tchu,	*Come to me with haste.*
Bo górami i lasami	*I fly over hills and valleys,*
Pędzę co mam tchu."	*Fast as e'er I can."*
"Hej! ptaszyno, tyś z nowiną.	*"Hail there, bird! Come you with tidings?*
Jaką wieziesz wieść?	*Of whom bring you news?*
Czy wesele, czy też wiele	*Wedding is it? Or do you have*
Musisz do mnie wieść?	*More you wish to tell?*

"Czarna skóra, czarne pióra;
To żałobny znak.
Ty z boleścią, smutną wieścią
Pędzisz do mnie tak."

"Matko moja, starość twoja
Będzie dla cię raj.
Syn twój drogi pobił wrogi
I poległ za kraj.

"Gdy za łupem i za trupem
Leciał tam gdzie bój,
Z wrogów klęski syn zwycięzki
Wołał do mnie twój:

" 'Hej ptaszyno! Tyś z nowiną
Od rodzinnych stron.
Leć do chatki mojej matki;
Donieś jej mój zgon.'

"I tak wołał i wnet skonał,
Lecz zwyciężył wprzód.
Na wawrzynie zwycięstw ginie,
Lecz wsławił swój ród."

Matka słucha a po chwili
Pada martwy trup.
Ponad synem słowik kwili;
Ponad matką kruk.

"*Black your skin and black your feathers;
Evil omen that.
Heartbreak you bring; pain and sorrow
Wing their way to me.*"

"*O dear Mother, your old age will
Be a paradise.
Your dear son the foe has vanquished;
He died for his land.*

"*In the midst of battle's fury,
He fought with stout heart;
And victorious over the foe,
Called he to me thus:*

" '*Hey there bird! You come with tidings
From familiar haunts.
To my mother's cottage fly now;
Tell her of my death.*'

"*Thus he called and then he died,
Though he conquered first.
Died he thus on vict'ry's laurel;
Gloried is his land.*"

*This she heard, and moments later
Lifeless did she fall.
O'er the son a nightingale weeps;
O'er her a raven.*[33]

147

74

Pokochał Się Młodzieniaszek W Pannie

A FAIR YOUTH FELL IN LOVE WITH A MAIDEN

Allegretto

Po - ko - chał się mło - dzie - nia - szek w pan -
A fair youth fell in love with a maid-

nie I chciał się z nią za - ślu - bić.
en And he ___ wished to mar - ry her.

Ro - dzi - ce wzbra - nia - li A bra - cia nie
"Nay, nay," said her par - ents. Her broth - ers for -

da - li; Ka - za - li mu we świat iść.
bade it And they sent him on his way.

Sung in 1940 by Mrs. John Krupski, who learned it in Buffalo.

Pokochał się młodzieniaszek w pannie	*A fair youth fell in love with a maiden;*
I chciał się z nią zaślubić.	*He wished to marry her.*
Rodzice wzbraniali,	*"Nay, nay," said her parents.*
A bracia nie dali;	*Her brothers forbade it*
Kazali mu we świat iść.	*And they sent him on his way.*

Młodzieniaszek ze świata powraca
I chciał się z kochanką widzieć.
Poszedł do pokoju,
Zastał matkę smutną;
Zaczeło mu serce drżeć.

"Jak się macie, moja pani matko?
Gdzież ta wasza córka jest?"
"Już dziś tydzień minął
Jak jest pochowana.
Jeszcze w sieni pościel jest.

"Młodzieniaszku, idź tam na cmentarzyk,
A tam nowy grób znajdziesz.
A na tem grobeczku
Trzy róże czerwone.
Te ci będą znajome."

Młodzieniaszek poszedł na cmentarzyk
I tam nowy grób znalazł.
Róże mu się kłaniały,
Znajomość dawały
Że tu kochanka leży.

"O kochanko, moja kochaneczko,
Ty tu leżysz w ciemnościach.
Już się nie ujrzemy
Aż na sąd staniemy
W rządzie Boga jasnościach."

When the youth returned from his wanderings,
He wished to see his love.
He saw her sad mother
As he entered the room.
His heart beat a dark omen.

"Mother of my loved one, how do you fare?
Where is your dear daughter?"
"It is seven days now
Since she has been buried.
See her linens in the hall.

"Young man, go to the cemetery.
There you'll find a new grave.
And upon this new grave
There are three red roses.
When you come, they'll nod to you."

So the youth bid the mother adieu
And he found the new grave.
Roses nodded to him,
Giving him the message
That his love lay buried there.

"My belovèd girl, O my dear heart,
In deep darkness you lie.
Not until God's judgment,
When we face our good Lord,
Shall we then meet once again."

75
Zasnął Jasio Na Murawie
JOHNNY SLUMBERED IN THE MEADOW

Za - snął Ja - sio na mu - ra - wie,
John - ny slum - bered in the mead - ow,

Śni - ło mu się jak na ja - wie;
And this dream he dreamed so clear - ly

Przy - le - cia - ła go - łę - bi - ca
That a dove flew down - ward to _____ him.

Ko - ło pół - no - cy księ - ży - ca. _____
'Twas a - bout the hour of mid - night. _____

Sung in 1940 by Mrs. Sophia Dziob, who learned it in Passaic, New Jersey.

Zasnął Jasio na murawie,	*Johnny slumbered in the meadow,*
Śniło mu się jak na jawie;	*And this dream he dreamed so clearly*
Przyleciała gołębica	*That a dove flew downward to him.*
Koło północy księżyca.	*'Twas about the hour of midnight.*
Jasio ze snu obudzony,	*Startled from his slumber, Johnny*
Idzie do wróżki zwieżonej.	*Hurried to a fortune teller.*
"Wróżko, wróżko, co mi powiesz	*"Fortune teller, what will you say*
Pierw nim się o mem śnie dowiesz?"	*Ere you hear about my strange dream?"*

Wróżka się na rozum wzięła;
Dwie szklanki wody przelała.
"Twoja panna ulubiona
Już nie będzie twoją żoną."

Idzie Janek rzewnęm krokiem,
Mija góry, mija lasy,
Aż popłacze i narzeka.
Wychodzi matka ze łzami.

"Witaj Janku. Witaj luby;
Jużeś nie nasz, tylko cudzy.
Twej miłej nie ma na świecie;
Wezmą cię za zięcia drudzy."

Poszedł Jasio do szkalaty;
Ubrali ją w białe szaty.
Ukląkł przed swą ulubioną;
Widzi ją w trumnie złożoną.

"A wy moje czarne oczki,
Czemu na mnie nie patrzycie?
I wy usta koralowe,
Czemu do mnie nie mówicie?"

Poszedł Jasio na katafalk;
Wielkie bóle go przejęły.
Bogu ducha oddał w ręce;
W jednem grobie ich złożyli.

She did get her wits about her;
In two glasses she poured water.
"Your beloved little sweetheart
Never will be wedded to you."

Mournfully then Johnny set forth,
Over mountains, through the forests,
Crying oft, and oft lamenting.
Tearfully her mother met him.

"Greetings, Johnny, greetings, loved one.
Ours no longer, but a stranger.
Gone forever is your sweetheart.
Son-in-law you'll be to others."

Johnny walked up to her casket;
In a shroud of white they dressed her.
There he knelt before his loved one;
Mournfully he looked upon her.

"O my dear belovèd dark eyes,
Why do you not look at me now?
Lips of coral, dear to my heart,
Why do you not speak to me now?"

He went to the catafalque;
Mortal pains o'ercame him near it.
To our Lord his soul he offered;
In one grave to rest they laid them.

76

A W Niedziele Porankiem[34]

EARLY, EARLY SUNDAY MORN

Con Grazia

A w nie - dzie - le po - ran - kiem,
Ear - ly, ear - ly Sun - day morn

Drob - no ro - sa pa - da - ła. Wy - szła,
When the dew drops gen - tly fell, Lo there

wy - szła pięk - na Kra - ko - wian - ka; Bia - łe
came a beau - ti - ful Cra - co - vienne Out to

1 ró - że zbie - ra - ła. **2** zbie - ra - ła.
gath - er ros - es white. *ros - es white.*

Sung in 1941 by Frank First, who learned it from his mother
and grandmother. They had learned it in Sonina, Poland.

A w niedziele porankiem,	*Early, early Sunday morn*
Drobno rosa padała.	*When the dew drops gently fell,*
Wyszła, wyszła piękna Krakowianka;	*Lo, there came a beautiful Cracovienne*
Białe róże zbierała.	*Out to gather roses white.*
Wyszła, wyszła piękna Krakowianka;	*Lo, there came a beautiful Cracovienne*
Białe róże zbierała.	*Out to gather roses white.*

Król się o niej dowiedział;
Liścik do niej napisał,
"Przyjedź, przyjedź, piękna Krakowianką,
Weź se króla za męża."

"Jam uboga sierota;
Nie mam srebra ni złota.
Tyś jest królu bardzo bogaty pan,
Weź se taką jakiś sam."

Król się na to rozgniewał;
Drógi liścik napisał,
"Przyjedź kacie, ścinaj Krakowianke
Bo ona mną wzgardziła."

Kat się o niej dowiedział;
Liścik do niej napisał,
"Przyjedź, przyjedź, piękna Krakowianką,
Weź se kata za męża."

"Nie byłam ja królową;
Nie będę też katową.
Przyjedź kacie, ścinaj moją szyje,
Bo tu mnie śmierć nie minie."

Gdy kat głowe jej ścinał,
Aniołek jej zaśpiewał,
"Nie płacz, nie płacz piękna Krakowianko,
Twoja dusza szczęśliwa."

News of her thus reached the king,
And he wrote a note to her,
"Come to me, my beautiful Cracovienne,
Wed a king and be his love."

"I am but an orphan poor,
Without gold or silver purse.
How can I wed you, a king majestic?
Choose a bride of royal rank."

Then the king fell in a rage
And another note he wrote,
"Hatchet man, behead the bold Cracovienne;
She has scorned a royal hand."

When the hatchet man learned this,
He, too, wrote a little note,
"Come to me, my beautiful Cracovienne;
Be a hatchet man's dear wife."

"Queenly crown did I reject;
I can scorn a hatchet man.
Come, I pray, behead me, hatchet man.
I cannot avoid my fate."

As the hatchet's blow did fall,
Lo, an angel's voice did sing,
"Weep not, weep not, beautiful Cracovienne,
Rest in Heav'n's peace, dear soul."

77

Jak Jechałem Z Ameryki
WHEN I JOURNEYED FROM AMERICA

Moderato

Jak je - cha - łem z A - me - ry - ki,
When I jour - neyed from A - mer - 'ca,

rit. **Vivace**

Jak je - cha - łem z A - me - ry - ki
When I jour - neyed from A - mer - 'ca

I z tej że - laz - nej fab - ry - ki,
And the found - ry where I la - bored,

I z tej że - laz - nej fab - ry - ki.
And the found - ry where I la - bored.

Sung in 1940 by Mrs. Sophia Dziob, who learned it from friends
in Passaic, New Jersey.

Jak jechałem z Ameryki,
Jak jechałem z Ameryki
I z tej żelaznej fabryki,
I z tej żelaznej fabryki.

Ręce moje dziękowały;
Do roboty zawsze stały.

When I journeyed from Amer'ca,
When I journeyed from Amer'ca
And the foundry where I labored,
And the foundry where I labored,

In pray'r my hands thanked our Father,
Hands that never shirked their labor.

Przyjechałem do Nef Jorka
Po szyfkartę do agenta.

Soon I came to New York City,
To the agent for my passage.

Agenci się mnie pytali
Czy wiozę trzysta dolary.

And the agents asked me if I
Had three hundred dollars with me.

"Nie pytajcie się mnie o to,
Bo ja wiozę srebro, złoto."

"Ask me not such foolish questions,
For I carry gold and silver."

Wyjechałem w środek morza;
Nic nie widzę, Matko Boża.

When I crossed the ocean midway,
No land could I see, sweet Virgin.

Szyf kapitan się nie nudził,
Tylko chodził, cieszył ludzi.

Our ship's captain was right busy,
Seeing, cheering all the people.

Jakżem ujżał miasto Hamburg,
To myślałem że sam Pan Bóg.

When I laid my eyes on Hamburg,
I thought I saw God Almighty.

A jakżem już wylądował,
Panu Bogu podziękował.

When at last I landed safely,
"Lord," I prayed, "I thank Thee for this."

"Dziękuje Ci, wielki Boże,
Żem przepłynął wielkie morze."

"O how grateful am I, dear God,
That I've crossed the ocean safely."

A z Hamburga do Berlina.
"Szynkareczko, daj mi wina."

Berlin came next after Hamburg.
"Barmaid, I will have some good wine."

A z Berlina do Krakowa,
Bo tam była żona moja.

Then I left Berlin for Krakow;
There my wife was waiting for me.

I dzieci mnie nie poznały,
Bo odemnie uciekały.

And my children did not know me,
For they fled from me, a stranger.

"Dzieci moje, ja wasz tata;
Nie był u was przez trzy lata."

"My dear children, I'm your papa;
Three long years I have not seen you."

78
Jechał Jeden Polak
A POLE WAS JOURNEYING

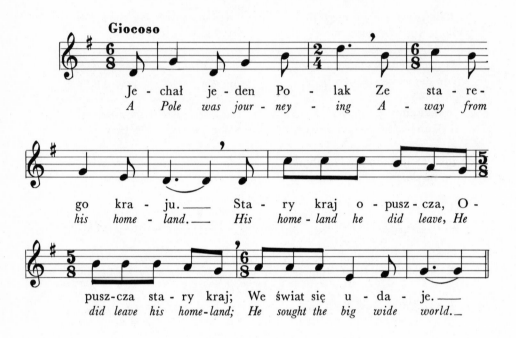

Giocoso

Je - chał je - den Po - lak Ze sta - re-
A Pole was jour - ney - ing A - way from

go kra - ju. ___ Sta - ry kraj o - pusz - cza, O-
his home - land. ___ His home - land he did leave, He

pusz - cza sta - ry kraj; We świat się u - da - je. ___
did leave his home - land; He sought the big wide world. _

Sung in 1940 by Mrs. Sophia Dziob, who learned it from friends
in Passaic, New Jersey.

Jechał jeden Polak	*A Pole was journeying*
Ze starego kraju.	*Away from his homeland.*
Stary kraj opuszcza,	*His homeland he did leave,*
Opuszcza stary kraj;	*He did leave his homeland;*
We świat się udaje.	*He sought the big wide world.*
Opuszcza stary kraj	*He left his native land,*
I kawałek chleba,	*The only bread he knew.*
I bierze na pomoc,	*For comfort and solace,*
I bierze na pomoc	*For comfort and solace,*
Matkę Boską z nieba.	*He took the Virgin Queen.*

Opuszcza stary kraj	He left his native land
I rodzonych ojców.	And all of his kinfolk.
W świat się udaje,	He sought the big wide world,
W świat się udaje	He sought the big wide world,
I sam nie wie poco.	Not knowing why he did.
Jak jedzie tak jedzie,	He traveled on and on,
Nigdy nie stopuje.	Nor did he stop midway.
Przyjdzie wielka burza,	A powerful storm came,
Przyjdzie wielka burza,	A powerful storm came
Szyfem powiewuje.	And tossed the ship about.
Szyfem powiewuje,	It tossed the ship about
Mało co wywróci.	And almost o'erturned it.
Co jednych odwiezie,	When one load was landed,
Co jednych odwiezie,	When one load was landed,
Po drugich się wróci.	It sailed for another.
Jak my przyjechali	When fin'lly we arrived
Do tej Kasengardy,	At Castle Garden's gates,
Zaraz-ci to poznać,	We recognized read'ly,
Zaraz-ci to poznać	We recognized read'ly
Który Polak każdy.	The face of every Pole.
Pobogłosław Boże	O God Almighty bless
Naszego cesarza	The emperor who ruled us
Że nas porozsyłał	And scattered us throughout,
Że nas porozsyłał	And scattered us throughout
Po tych cudzych krajach.	These lonely foreign lands.
Po tych cudzych krajach,	These lonely foreign lands,
I to po Anglikach.	And English ones at that,
Bieda nie jednemu,	For woe to him who knows,
Bieda nie jednemu	For woe to him who knows
Co niezna języka.	Not how to speak English.
W Ameryce dobrze	American life is fine
Jak idzie robota.	When there are jobs for all
Piwka się napije,	With beer to soothe dry throats,
Piwka się napije	With beer to soothe dry throats
Przyjdzie sobota.	On Sat'rday afternoons.
W Ameryce dobrze	American life is fine,
Czy mały czy duży.	No matter who you are.
Piwka się napije,	There's beer to soothe dry throats,
Piwka się napije,	There's beer to soothe dry throats,
Cygara zakurzy.	Cigars to puff with ease.

W Ameryce dobrze
I śmiało i śmiało.
Ale w Ameryce,
Ale w Ameryce
Poczciwości mało.

Poczciwości mało,
Wesołości dużo.
Każda panna chodzi,
Każda panna chodzi
Jak kwiateczek róży.

American life is fine
In freedom's atmosphere,
But here in America,
But here in America
Life can be most lonely.

Yes, lonely is our life,
Though gaiety abounds.
Each miss promenades here,
Each miss promenades here
As if she were a rose.

IV

*There is no theme which a singer cannot feel and,
feeling it, does not fashion into song.*
He greets the Holy Infant with song.
*He brings joy to the wedding festival and a finale to the
harvest.*
*Like the drummer with his beat, with his song he gives
pulse to the dance.*

79
Przylecieli Tak Śliczni Anieli
ANGELS OF GREAT BEAUTY CAME DOWN TO EARTH

Przy - le - cie - li   tak ślicz - ni   a - nie - li;
An - gels   of   great   beau - ty   came   down   to   earth,

Wszysz - cy w bie - li,   zło - te piór - ka   mie - li.
Robed   in   pure   white,   winged   in   gold - en   feath - ers.

Przy - nieś - li   nam   we - so - łą   no - wi - nę;
Tid - ings   of   joy   they   did   bring   to   all   men

Pan - na Czys - ta   zro - dzi - ła   Dzie - ci - nę.
That   the   Vir - gin   birthed   the   Ho - ly   In - fant.

A carol, sung in 1941 by Frank First, who learned it from his sister,
who had learned it in Sonina, Poland.

Przylecieli tak śliczni anieli;
Wszyscy w bieli, złote piórka mieli.
Przynieśli nam wesołą nowinę;
Panna czysta zrodziła Dziecinę.
Przynieśli nam wesołą nowinę;
Panna Czysta zrodziła Dziecinę.

Angels of great beauty came down to earth,
Robed in pure white, winged in golden feathers.
Tidings of joy they did bring to all men
That the Virgin birthed the Holy Infant.
Tidings of joy they did bring to all men
That the Virgin birthed the Holy Infant.

A zrodziwszy, w pieluszki powiła;
A powiwszy, na sianku złożyła.
Leży, leży Jezuz malusieńki;
Leży, leży Jezuz malusieńki.

Zdjęła Panna swój rąbeczek z głowy;
Ściele w żłobku Panu Jezusowi.
"A lulaj-że, drogie serce moje,
Bo Cię kocham tak jak życie swoje."

Pastuszkowie grajcie Stwórcy swemu,
W tej stajence dla was zrodzonemu.
Proścież Pana by wam błogosławił
Tu na ziemi a w niebie postawił.

When He came, in swaddling clothes she wrapped Him.
Having wrapped Him, on the hay she laid Him.
There He lies, our tiny Infant Jesus.
There He lies, our tiny Infant Jesus.

From her head, the Virgin slipped her kerchief.
Smoothly spread it o'er the crib for Jesus.
"Lu-lay, lu-lay, my dear Infant, lu-lay.
Dear as life to me Thou art, dear Jesus."

Shepherds, come and play for your Creator.
Born here in this manger is your Savior.
Pray the Lord that He grant you His blessing
Here on earth and hereafter in Heaven.

80

Tusząc Pasterze Że Dzień Blisko

SHEPHERDS EXPECTING THE BREAK OF DAY

Alla Marcia

Tu - sząc pas - te - rze że dzień blis - ko,
Shep - herds ex - pect - ing the break of day,

Wyg - na - li ow - ce na past - wis - ko
Out to the pas - ture herd - ed their sheep,

Z o - bo - ry, — z o - bo - ry, — z o - bo - ry.
From the fold, — from the fold, — from the fold.

Za - pę - dzi - li pod bo - ry, pod bo - ry.
On they drove them, toward the wood, toward the wood

Tra - fi - li na do - brą tra - wę; Po - kład - li się
Where the grass was green and ten - der. On the grass the

na mu - ra - wę; Pos - nę - li, pos - nę - li.
shep - herds rest - ed, And they slept, and they slept.

A carol, sung in 1941 by Frank First, who learned it from his grandmother,
who had learned it in Sonina, Poland.

Tusząc pasterze, że dzień blisko,
Wygnali owce na pastwisko
Z obory, z obory, z obory.
Zapędzili pod bory, pod bory.
Trafili na dobrą trawę;
Pokładli się na murawę;
Posnęli, posnęli.
A bydło jadło, jadło, jadło,
A bydło jadło, jadło, jadło;
Potem się pokładło,
Potem się pokładło.

Shepherds, expecting the break of day,
Out to the pasture herded their sheep,
From the fold, from the fold, from the fold.
On they drove them, toward the wood, toward the wood
Where the grass was green and tender.
On the grass the shepherds rested,
And they slept, and they slept.
And the cows grazed and grazed and grazed there,
And the cows grazed and grazed and grazed there,
Then they, too, settled down,
Then they, too, settled down.

Wilk zaś wypadłszy od ugoru,
Zagnał im owce aż do boru.
O bieda, o bieda, o bieda!
Kozom się wilk paść nie da, paść nie da.
Podusiwszy już koźlęta,
Suwa jeszcze po jagnięta.
Masz tobie, masz tobie!
Już trzoda cała, cała, cała
W rozsypkę pójść miała.

Bursting upon them, came a fierce wolf.
It drove the sheep away to the woods.
O what grief! O what grief! O what grief!
It did worry all the goats, all the goats.
Having strangled every kid,
It moved onward toward the lambs.
O alas! O alas!
Now the whole flock, whole flock, the whole flock
Would be gone, would be gone.

Lecz porwawszy się ze snu Kuba	*Startled from deep sleep, Jake was amazed,*
Spojrzawszy, widzi że tu zguba.	*For as he looked up, he saw the ruin.*
"A to co? A to co? A to co?"	*"What is this? What is this? What is this?"*
Jak zakrzyknie swą mocą, swą mocą,	*He then bellowed forth with might, forth with might,*
"Nieszczęsne mych lat momenta!	*"Darkest moment of my life!*
A kędyż są me jagnięta?	*Where O where are all my poor lambs?*
Już po nich, już po nich."	*Gone alas! Gone alas!"*
A anioł leci, leci, leci;	*He saw an angel flying, flying,*
Jasnością swą świeci.	*Giving forth radiant light.*
Powoli potem słów dochodzi	*Gradually he heard these words from above,*
Że anioł nuci, "Bóg się rodzi!"	*An angel voice sang, "Christ is born."*
I wstaje, i wstaje, i wstaje,	*He then did rise, he then did rise, he did rise,*
Serce sobie dodaje, dodaje.	*Courage warmed his frightened heart, frightened heart.*
Widzi gwiazdę że stanęła,	*Steadfast star he saw a-shining,*
Jasność wielka ogarnęła	*With a light of wond'rous glory*
Betlejem, Betlejem.	*Over all Bethlehem.*
I woła, "Trwoga, trwoga, trwoga!	*He cried, "Behold! Behold! Behold!*
Hey! wstańcie dla Boga!"	*All arise! God is come!"*
Wnet do Betlejem poskoczyli,	*Then they all hurried to Bethlehem,*
Bogu swe trzody polecili.	*Trusting their flocks to Almighty's care.*
Ciekawi, ciekawi, ciekawi	*They were curious, they were curious, curious,*
Święte Dziecię gdzie bawi, gdzie bawi.	*"Holy Infant, where art Thou? Where art Thou?"*
W szopie gdzie są osioł z wołem,	*Sharing with the ass and oxen,*
Na sianeczku leży społem.	*He lies on the manger's sweet hay.*
A tu mróz, a tu mróz.	*O the cold! O the cold!*
Stwórca Bóg płacze, płacze, placze,	*And our Child cries and cries and cries,*
A stworzenie skacze.	*While the beasts leap about.*
W tem przyskoczyli do nóg Pana,	*Awe-stricken shepherds rushed to our Lord;*
Pasterze padli na kolana.	*Humbly these shepherds fell to their knees.*
Wesoło, wesoło, wesoło,	*Joyously, joyously, joyously,*
Otoczyli Go w koło, Go w koło.	*They encircled Him that night, Him that night;*
Darami Go obsypali,	*Gifts they heaped on Christ the Infant,*
Bydła, ptastwa nadawali	*Birds and beasts they offered Jesus*
Dostatkiem, dostatkiem.	*Without end, without end.*
A sami dalej, dalej, dalej	*They, the while, on and on, on and on,*
Pioseneczki śpiewali.	*Sang to Him, sang to Him.*

Miał Bartek dudy, Grzela skrzypki;
Stanąwszy zdala od kolebki,
Oj rznęli, oj rznęli, oj rznęli,
Oj co tylko sił mieli, sił mieli.
Struny się im pozrywały,
Dudy się też popękały.
Oj grali, oj grali,
"O dyna, dyna, dyna, dyna,
Gdzie mała Dziecina?"

A chociaż nogę Stach wywinął,
A Banachowi kolpak zginął,
Nie stali, nie stali, nie stali,
Lecz co żywo skakali, skakali,
Z swych podkówek ognia dając,
Zawsze "Ho! Ho!" wykrzykując.
A Maciek, a Maciek,
"Hej! da da! da da! da da! da da!"
Piosneczki wynajda.

Bartek played bagpipes, Grzela fiddled.
They stood with rev'rence near the Christ Child.
But they piped, sawed and fiddled joyously,
So much vigor they did use, they did use
That their fiddle strings were broken,
Burstèd were their bagpipes mighty.
On they played! On they played!
"O dyna, dyna, dyna, dyna,
Where art Thou, Holy Child?"

Even though Stanley twisted his leg,
Even though Banach lost his fur cap,
Stop they did not, stop they did not, no not they.
But with great joy, on they danced, on they danced.
Sparks flew brightly from their heels
As they called out, "Ho! Ho! Ho! Ho!"
Matthew too, Matthew too,
With his "Hey! da da! da da! da da!"
Fine new songs he composed.

81

W Tej Kolędzie Kto Dziś Będzie[35]

JOIN US IN THIS FESTIVE CAROL

With accent

W tej ko - lę - dzie kto dziś bę - dzie Każ - dy
Join us in this fes - tive car - ol And be

się u - cie - szy. A kto co ma po - da - ro - wać
joy - ful with us. Bring what gifts your heart can of - fer

Nie - chaj pręd - ko śpie - szy. Dać da - ry
And do has - ten with them. Give of your

z tej mia - ry Dla Pa - na ma - łe - go, By na - był
heart's full - ness For the ti - ny In - fant, That you may

po śmier - ci Zba - wie - nia wiecz - ne - go.
one day have Sal - va - tion e - ter - nal.

Sung in 1941 by Frank First, who learned it from his grandmother,
who had learned it in Sonina, Poland.

W tej kolędzie kto dziś będzie
Każdy się ucieszy.
A kto co ma podarować
Niechaj prędko śpieszy.
Dać dary z tej miary
Dla Pana małego,
By nabył po śmierci
Zbawienia wiecznego.
Dać dary z tej miary
Dla Pana małego,
By nabył po śmierci
Zbawienia wiecznego.

Kuba stary przyniósł dary,
Masła na talerzu.
Sobek parę gołąbeczków
Takich jeszcze w pierzu.
Wziął Tomek gomołek
I jajeczko gęsie.
Bartek nie miał co dać;
Dobre chęci niesie.

Walek sprawiał tłuste raki
Nierychło z wieczora.
Nałożywszy dwie kobiele,
Biegł z niemi przez pola
Aż tu strach napotkał
Walka nieboraka;
Staneły dwa wilki
Niedaleko krzaka.

Gdy obaczył owe gady,
Podskoczył wysoko.
Wielkiem strachem przestraszony,
Wybił sobie oko.
Uciekał przez krzaki;
Podarł se chodaki;
A wilki mu targali
Z kobeliny raki.

Przeto wszyscy oddawajmy
Temu Panu dary.
Pan to dobry, wszystkiem szczodry,
Przyjmie nas do chwały.
Niech będzie, niech będzie
Jezus pochwalony,
Który jest, który jest
W żłobie położony.

Join us in this festive carol
And be joyful with.us.
Bring what gifts your heart can offer
And do hasten with them.
Give of your heart's fullness
For the tiny Infant,
That you may one day have
Salvation eternal.
Give of your heart's fullness
For the tiny Infant,
That you.may one day have
Salvation eternal.

Jake, the old one, gave what he could,
Butter on a platter;
And Sebastian brought two pigeons
Plumed in their fine feathers.
Tom came with curds and whey
And an egg his goose laid.
Bart had nought he could give,
So he came with good will.

Val came with the crabs that he caught
Early in the evening.
He arranged them in two baskets
And then hurried with them.
But alas! What a fright
Val did have, the poor wretch.
Wolves, a pair, he saw there,
Standing in the bushes.

When he saw the evil creatures,
He leaped, deeply frightened.
And thus frightened, he ran madly
Till he scratched his eyes out.
Running through the underbrush,
He wore out his last clogs,
While the wolves snarled and tore
Crabs out of his baskets.

Let us all then give what we can,
Gifts to our good Shepherd.
God is good, munificent, too;
We shall see His glory.
God be praised, God be praised,
Glory to wee Jesus
Who lies here, who lies here
In this hay-filled manger.

82

Dnia Jednego O Północy
'TWAS ONCE UPON A MIDNIGHT CLEAR

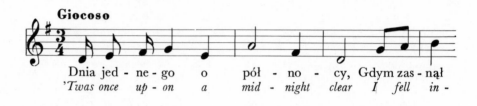

Giocoso

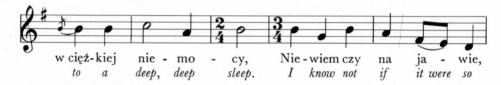

Dnia jed - ne - go o pół - no - cy, Gdym zas - nął
'Twas once up - on a mid - night clear I fell in -

w cięż-kiej nie - mo - cy, Nie-wiem czy na ja - wie,
to a deep, deep sleep. I know not if it were so

Czy mi się śni - ło Że we - dle mej bu - dy Słoń - ce
Or wheth - er I dreamed That o - ver my cot - tage Sun - shine

świe - ci - ło. Nie wiem czy na ja - wie, Czy mi się śni -
strong - ly beamed. I know not if 'twere so Or wheth - er I

ło Że we - dle mej bu - dy Słoń - ce świe - ci - ło.
dreamed That o - ver my cot - tage Sun-shine strong - ly beamed.

Sung in 1941 by Frank First, who learned it from his mother,
who had learned it in Sonina, Poland.

Dnia jednego o północy,	'Twas once upon a midnight clear
Gdym zasnął w ciężkiej niemocy,	I fell into a deep, deep sleep.
Nie wiem czy na jawie,	I know not if it were so
Czy mi się śniło	Or whether I dreamed
Że wedle mej budy	That over my cottage
Słońce świeciło.	Sunshine strongly beamed.
Nie wiem czy na jawie,	I know not if 'twere so
Czy mi się śniło	Or whether I dreamed
Że wedle mej budy	That over my cottage
Słońce świeciło.	Sunshine strongly beamed.
Sam się czemprędzej porwałem	Quickly I arose from my bed
I na drugich zawołałem,	And I called to all who slept,
Na Kube, na Maćka,	To Jacob, Mat also,
I na Kaźimierza,	As well as Casimer,
By wstali czemprędzej	Quickly to get them up
Mówić pacierze.	And to say their prayers.
Nie zaraz się podźwignęli,	How hard it was to waken them,
Bo oni bardzo zasnęli.	For their slumber was hard and deep.
Alem ich po trochu	One by one I pulled them
Wziął za czupryne	By their tousled hair,
By wstali przywitać	Bidding them arise and
Boga Dziecine.	Greet the new born Babe.
Kazimierz bowiem wszystko słyszał,	'Twas Casimer who heard the news
Bo na słomie w budzie dyszał.	As he lay in the straw-filled bed;
Ale nam od strachu	So struck with awe was he,
Nie chciał powiedzieć.	He would tell us nought.
Na Maćka wskazywał,	Pointing to Matt, he said,
"Ten musi wiedzieć."	"He it is who knows."
"No Macieju, ty nam powiesz	"Matt, tell us everything you heard
Ponieważ ty sam wszystko wiesz."	You are the one who saw and heard."
"Widziałem, widziałem	"I did see it, see it,
Dziwne widzenie.	Truly a strange sight.
Szłyszałem, szłyszałem	I did hear it, hear it,
Anielskie pienie.	Angel voices sing.
"Bo mi sam Anioł powiedział	"Yea truly, did the angel say,
Gdym na słomie w budzie siedział,	As there upon the straw I sat,
W Betlejem narodził,	'Born is He in Bethlehem,
W tak sławnym mieście,	Town of great glory.'
Więc Jego czemprędzej	Therefore let us hasten
Przywitać bieżcie."	To the Holy Child."

169

"Niech weźmie Stasiek fujarę,
A Szymek gołąbków parę.
A Maciek będzie stał
U drzwi z obuchem
Bo się tam nie zmieści
Z swym wielkim brzuchem."

Porwawszy się, biegli drogą
Gdzie widzieli jasność srogą
W Betlejem miasteczku
Gdzie Dziecie było
Ktorę się dla wszystkich
Z nieba zjawiło.

Ubiegliśmy zaraz do szopy;
Uściskaliśmy Mu stopy.
Jam dobył fujary,
A Kuba rogu;
Graliśmy co żywo
Na chwałe Bogu.

Stach do brony wiązał struny;
Sobek skakał jak sparzony;
A Maciek musiał stać
U drzwi z obuchem
Bo się nie mógł zmieścić
Z swym wielkim brzuchem.

"Jacek chudy zagrał w dudy,
A my w taniec koło budy.
A ty Michale,
Zagraj na flecie,
A za to kolędę
Dobrą weźmiecie."

Na niczem nam nie zbywało,
Z szopy nam się iść nie chciało,
Aleśmy ustąpić
W prędce musieli,
Gdyśmy trzech Monarchów
Jadąc ujrzeli.

"Now take your shepherd's pipes, Stanley;
And you, Simon, fair doves a pair.
But Matt will have to stand
At the open door,
For how can he fit in
With his stomach huge?"

Rising quickly, the road they took
Where the awesome bright light led them
To fair Bethlehem town
Where the Infant lay,
Born for all mankind, and
Come from Heaven above.

The lowly manger we did reach;
His wee feet we caressed with joy.
I reached for my bagpipes,
And Matt for his horn.
Merrily we played on,
Praising our good Lord.

Stan's harrow strung with fiddle strings,
Sebastian danced with joyful glee,
While Matt stood at the door,
Hatchet in his hand,
For how could he fit in
With his stomach huge?

"Lean Hyacinth, your bagpipes play!
Around the hut we'll dance.
While you there, Michael!
Play upon your flute,
And your reward will be
Blessings of the day."

Thus merrily we spent our time,
Loathe to leave the wee Holy Child,
But depart we had to,
Hurriedly at that,
When we saw the Three Kings
Coming to see Him.

83
Do Ślubejku Jedziewa
NOW WE'RE ON OUR WAY TO CHURCH

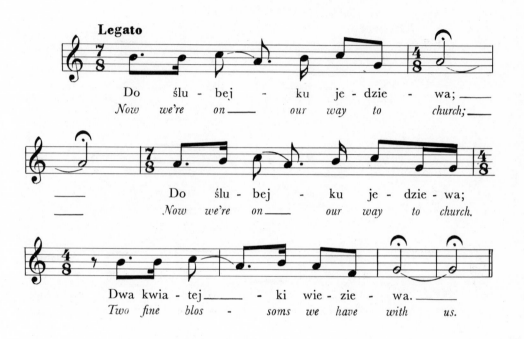

Do ślu - bej - ku je - dzie - wa; ___
Now we're on ___ our way to church; ___

___ Do ślu - bej - ku je - dzie - wa;
Now we're on ___ our way to church.

Dwa kwia - tej ___ - ki wie - zie - wa. ___
Two fine blos - soms we have with us.

Sung in 1940 by Mrs. Helen Poplawska, who learned it in Poland.

Do ślubejku jedziewa;	*Now we're on our way to church;*
Do ślubejku jedziewa;	*Now we're on our way to church.*
Dwa kwiatejki wieziewa.	*Two fine blossoms we have with us.*
Jeden kwiatek różowy	*Lo, one blossom is a rose,*
A drugi kalinowy.	*And the other flower is white.*
W naszem grodzie kwitnie ziele;	*In our garden herbs are blooming;*
W naszem rodzie dziś wesele.	*In our fam'ly there's a wedding.*
A kto nam zawiduje,	*He who comes to visit us;*
Niech se córkę wychoduje.	*May he raise a healthy daughter.*

84

Oj Siadaj, Siadaj, Moje Kochanie[36]

O COME BE SEATED, BELOVED OF MY HEART

(See number 85)

"Oj, sia - daj, sia - daj, mo - je ko - cha -
O come be seat - ed, be - loved of my

nie. Nic nie po - mo - że two - je pła - ka - nie.
heart. Noth - ing will help now, not e - ven your tears.

Nic nie na - da, nie po - mo - że; Sto - ją ko - nie,
None can aid you; none can help you. Wait - ing hors - es,

sto - ją wo - zy Po - na - wra - ca - ne."
wait - ing wag - ons Are fac - ing the church."

Sung in 1940 by Mrs. Helen Poplawska, who learned it in Poland.

"Oj, siadaj, siadaj, moje kochanie.
Nic nie pomoże twoje płakanie.
Nic nie nada, nie pomoże;
Stoją konie, stoją wozy
Ponawracane."

"O come be seated, beloved of my heart.
Nothing will help now, not even your tears.
None can aid you; none can help you.
Waiting horses, waiting wagons
Are facing the church."

"Jeszcze nie będę z wami jechała,
Bom ja się z tatą nie żegnała.
Bądźcie zdrowi, drogi tato,
Com robiła z wami całe lato.
Teraz nie będę."

(Repeat stanza number 1.)

"Jeszcze nie będę z wami jechała,
Bom ja się z mamo nie żegnała.
Dziękuję ci, moja matko,
Żeś mnie wychowała gładko.
Teraz nie będziesz."

(Repeat stanza number 1.)

*"I am not ready to ride forth with you.
I have not yet bid my papa farewell.
Be of good health, my dear papa.
I've worked with you through the summer;
No more will I help."*

(Repeat stanza number 1.)

*"I am not ready to ride forth with you.
I have not yet bid my mother farewell.
I now thank you, my dear mother,
For the loving care you gave me.
Your work now is o'er."*

(Repeat stanza number 1.)

85
Przed Dom Przyjechali
NOW THEY STOP AT HER HOUSE
(Variant of number 84)

Con brio

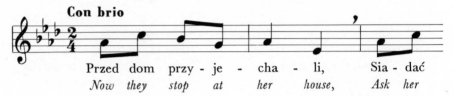

Przed dom przy - je - cha - li, Sia - dać
Now they stop at her house, Ask her

ji ka - za - li, Do koś - cio - ła
to be seat - ed, For 'tis time to

ślu - bo - wać. "Ja się mu - szę
go to ___ church. "O dear, I must

wró - cić, Ro - dzi - ców prze - pro - sić
turn back, Beg my par - ents' par - don,

Na sto kroć po - dzię - ko - wać.
And thank them a hun - dred - fold.

Sung in 1940 by Mrs. Victoria Zdziebko, who learned it in Turek, Poland.

Przed dom przyjechali,
Siadać ji kazali,
Do kościoła ślubować.
"Ja się muszę wrócić,
Rodziców przeprosić
Na stokroć podziękować.

"Dziękuję ci, ojcze,
Dziękuję ci, mamo,
Dziękuję na stokroć wam.
Żeście mnie zrodzili,
Pięknie wychowali.
Teraz idę od was precz."

Now they stop at her house,
Ask her to be seated,
For 'tis time to go to church.
"O dear, I must turn back,
Beg my parents' pardon,
And thank them a hundred fold.

"I thank you, dear Father,
I thank you, dear Mamma,
I thank you a hundred fold
For the life you've giv'n me,
And for the good breeding.
Now I'm leaving you, my dears."

86

Jak Pójdziemy Do Kościoła
WHEN WE GET TO CHURCH TODAY

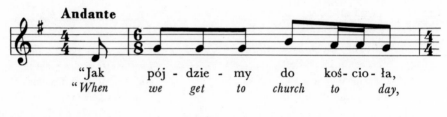

"Jak   pój - dzie - my   do   koś- cio- ła,
"When   we   get   to   church   to   day,

Już jes - teś mo - ja."   "Jesz - czem ci nie two-ja;
You will then be mine."   "I am not yours, not yet;

Jesz - czem so - bie wol - na,   Mię - dzy pan - na -
I am still free, quite free   A - mong the young

mi, pan - na - mi,   Mię - dzy pan - na - mi."
maids, the young maids,   A - mong the young maids."

Sung in 1941 by Mrs. John Krupski, who learned it from her mother
in Buffalo.

"Jak pójdziemy do kościoła,
Już jesteś moja."

"Jeszczem ci nie twoja;
Jeszczem sobie wolna,
Między pannami, pannami,
Między pannami."

"When we get to church today,
You will then be mine."

"I am not yours, not yet;
I am still free, quite free
Among the young maids, the young maids,
Among the young maids."

87

Młody Panie Nasz

WHERE IS OUR YOUNG GROOM?

Młó - dy pa - nie nasz, Czy cię tu nie -
Where   is   our   young   groom?   Is   he   not   with

ma?   Wyj - dzij,   wyj - dzij   z ka - ra - fecz - ką.
us?   Come   out,   come   out   with   the   ca - rafe.

Po - częs - tuj nas   Go - rza - łecz - ką.
Fill   our   glass - es   With   fine   spir - its.

Ład - ną żon - kę masz.   Ład - ną żon - kę masz.
Hail   to   your   fair   bride!   Hail   to   your   fair   bride!

Sung in 1940 by Mrs. Victoria Zdziebko, who learned it in her native
village of Turek, Poland.

Młody panie nasz,	*Where is our young groom?*
Czy cię tu niema?	*Is he not with us?*
Wyjdzij, wyjdzij	*Come out, come out*
Z karafeczką.	*With the carafe.*
Poczęstuj nas	*Fill our glasses*
Gorzałeczką.	*With fine spirits.*
Ładną żonkę masz.	*Hail to your fair bride!*
Ładną żonkę masz.	*Hail to your fair bride!*

88

Ach Mój Wianku Rozmarynie[37]

O MY GARLAND OF ROSEMARY

(See number 90)

Ach mój wian - ku roz - ma - ry - nie,
O my gar - land of rose - mar - y,

Com cię sia - ła na za - go - nie.
In my gar - den I have sown you.

Już cię wię - cej siać nie bę - dę
I shall nev - er plant you a - gain,

Bo już te - raz za mąż i - dę.
For to - day I shall be mar - ried.

Sung in 1940 by Mrs. John Krupski, who learned it from her mother in Buffalo.

Ach mój wianku rozmarynie,	*O my garland of rosemary,*
Com cię siała na zagonie.	*In my garden I have sown you.*
Już cię więcej siać nie będę	*I shall never plant you again,*
Bo już teraz za mąż idę.	*For today I shall be married.*

Niech cię sieje młodsza siostra
Która jeszcze za mąż nie szła.
Ach mój wianku z białej róży,
Już mi więcej świat nie służy.

Innym służy a mnie nie chce.
Opłakane moje życie.
. . . .
. . . .

Let my younger sister plant you;
She is still an unwed maiden.
O my wreath of pure white roses,
Life has no more pleasure for me.

Life serves others well, but ah me,
Ever tearfilled has my life been.
. . . .
. . . .

89
Dwanaście Listeczek
THERE ARE TWELVE GREEN LEAFLETS

Moderato

Dwa - naś - cie lis - te - czek Na czer -
There are twelve green leaf - lets *Grow - ing*

wo - nej ró - ży. Dwa - naś - cie a - nio -
on a red rose. *There are twelve* *good an -*

łów Pan - nie mło - dej słu - ży.
gels *Who* *are* *guard - ing* *our* *bride.*

Sung in 1940 by Mrs. Sophia Dziob, who learned it in Passaic, New Jersey,
where it was sung at a folk wedding just before the bridal couple left for the church.

Dwanaście listeczek	*There are twelve green leaflets*
Na czerwonej róży.	*Growing on a red rose.*
Dwanaście aniołów	*There are twelve good angels*
Pannie młodej służy.	*Who are guarding our bride.*
Pierwszy anioł niesie	*The first angel carries*
Ruciany wianeczek.	*A garland of green rue.*
Drugi anioł niesie	*And the second angel*
Złoty pierścioneczek.	*Brings a ring of pure gold.*
Trzeci anioł niesie	*The third angel carries*
Lilie pachnące.	*Lilies of sweet fragrance.*
Czwarty anioł niesie	*And the fourth angel brings*
Świece gorejące	*A bright-burning candle.*

Piąty anioł niesie	*The fifth angel brings her*
Miłość i małżeństwo.	*Love and happy marriage.*
Szósty anioł niesie	*And the sixth angel brings*
I błogosławieństwo.	*Blessings from above.*

Drugie sześć aniołów	*And the six remaining*
Służą nad jej głową.	*Hover o'er the bride's head,*
Trzymają koronę	*And they hold a gold crown*
Jakby nad królową.	*As if she were a queen.*

Pamiętaj Jasieńku,	*Now remember, Johnny,*
Żebyś jej nie bijał,	*Never strike your young bride,*
Bo będziesz żałował	*Or the day you will rue*
Jak ją sponiewierasz.	*When she'll be ill-treated.*

Teraz ty ją bierzesz	*You are taking her now*
Jak różę czerwoną.	*Lovely as a red rose.*
A później będziesz miał	*Later she may well be*
Jak trawę zieloną.	*Wasted and without bloom.*

90

Pomału Ją Rozbierajcie[37]

GENTLY UNVEIL HER, UNVEIL HER

(Variant of number 88)

Po - ma - łu ją roz - bie -
Gen - tly un - veil her, un -

raj —- cie. Za wło - sy ją, za
veil — her. Do not, O do not,

wło - sy — ją Nie tar - gaj —- cie.
we pray — you, Pull her tress — - es.

Sung in 1941 by Frank First, who learned it from his mother-in-law.
She had learned it in her native town, Krosno, Poland.

"Pomału ją rozbierajcie.
Za włosy ją, za włosy ją
Nie targajcie.
Za włosy ją, za włosy ją
Nie targajcie.

"Bo ją mama wychowała.
Za włosy ją, za włosy ją
Nie targała."

"Ach mój miły rozmarynie,
Com cię siała, com cię siała
Na zagonie.

"Gently unveil her, unveil her.
Do not, O do not, we pray you,
Pull her tresses.
Do not, O do not, we pray you,
Pull her tresses.

"Tenderly her mother reared her.
Never did she pull her tresses.
Never, never."

"O my dear wreath, rosemary wreath.
I have sown thee, yea, I've sown thee
In the garden.

"Już cię więcej siać nie będę,
Bo już dzisiaj, bo już dzisiaj
Za mąż wyjdę.

"Niech cię sieją młodsze siostry
Które jeszcze, które jeszcze
Za mąż nieszły.

"Chociaż nie szły, ale pójdą.
Rozmarynu, rozmarynu
Sieć nie będą."

"*Never again shall I plant thee.
Now is the day, yea, 'tis the day
Of my marriage.*

"*Younger sisters will now plant thee.
They are not yet, yea, they are not yet
Pledged to marry.*

"*They will soon be married also,
Then they will not plant thee either,
My rosemary.*"

91

Matulu, Tatulu![38]

DEAR MOTHER! O FATHER!

Moderato

"Ma - tu - lu, ta - tu - lu!__ Ot - wie - raj__ -
"Dear Moth - er! O Fath - er!__ O - pen wide__

cie wro - ta. Nio - są nam tu wie___ -niec
the gates now. They bring us a gar___ -land

Ze szcze - re - go zło - ta." "Graj - że graj - ku,
Which they made of pure gold." "Play there, fid - dler!

A we - so - ło! Bo dziś wszyz - cy Sta - niem
Play with spir - it. We shall all dance, Cir - cle

w ko - ło. Płon przy - nieś__ - lym, Płon!"__
gai - ly. Fruits of field__ We bring!"__

Sung in 1940 by Mrs. Helen Poplawska, who learned it while in a
convent in Poland.

"Matulu, tatulu!
Otwierajcie wrota.
Niosą nam tu wieniec
Ze szczerego złota."

Refren:
"Graj-że grajku,
A wesoło!
Bo dziś wszyscy
Staniem w koło.
Płon przynieślym,
Płon!"

"Bodaj się te ręce
Z naszemi złączyły,
Co ten piękny wieniec
Tak cudnie uwiły."

"Dear Mother! O Father!
Open wide the gates now.
They bring us a garland
Which they made of pure gold."

Refrain:
"Play there, fiddler!
Play with spirit.
We shall all dance,
Circle gaily.
Fruits of field
We bring!"

"Let us join our hands now
With those of the gleaners,
Who have made this garland
With such wondrous beauty."

92

Ja Za Wodą, Ty Za Wodą[39]

I'M ON ONE BANK, YOU THE OTHER

Moderato

"Ja za wo-dą, ty za wo-dą.
"*I'm on one bank, you the oth-er.*

Jak-ze ja ci___ gę-by po-dom?
How then can I___ reach your warm___ lips?

Po-dom ci ja na lis-tec-ku; Mas-ci
A kiss I'll send you on this leaf; There you

Ma-ryś, ko-cha-nec-ku." O-be-rek, o be-
have it, Ma-ry dar-ling." O-be-rek, mad-ly

re-cek;___ Ma-zu-rek, ma-zu-re-cek;
whirl-ing;___ And a ma-zur, danced with joy;

Ku-ja-wiak, ku-ja-wia-cek;
Ku-ya-viak, gay ku-ya-viak;

Za - tań - ce - my so - bie, Raz, wraz, wraz!
Ma - ry,— be my part - ner, One, two, three!

Sung in 1940 by Adam Bartosz, who learned it from peasants
in southern Poland.

"Ja za wodą, ty za wodą.
Jakze ja ci gęby podom?
Podom ci ja na listecku;
Mas-ci Maryś, kochanecku."

Refren:
Oberek, oberecek;
Mazurek, mazurecek;
Kujawiak, kujawiacek;
Zatańcemy sobie,
Raz, wraz, wraz!

"Zebyś ty mnie jak ja tobie,
Daly byśmy gęby sobie;
Ale ty mnie kepsko zycyz.
Ja do ciebie a ty ksycys."

"Na kapuście drobne liście.
Nie dom gęby łorganiście.
Łorganista zapisuje
Ile razy pocałuje."

Maryś na piec; Maciek za nią.
Wywalyli kluski z banią.
"Pocozeście sie gonili
I te kluski wywalyli?"

"Ja nie winna; Maciek winien
Bo mnie ścigać nie powinien."
"Nie ja winien; Maryś winna
Bo uciekać nie powinna."

"*I'm on one bank, you the other.
How then can I reach your warm lips?
A kiss I'll send you on this leaf;
There you have it, Mary darling.*"

Refrain:
*Oberek, madly whirling;
And a mazur, danced with joy;
Kuyaviak, gay kuyaviak;
Mary, be my partner,
One, two three!*

"*If you love me as I love you,
We would press our lips together;
But you do not think much of me.
I reach for you and you cry out.*"

"*Tiny leaves grow on the cabbage.
I will not kiss an organist,
He'll remember all too well
Ev'ry kiss that I do give him.*"

*She leaped stove-ward, Mat dashed for her.
Down came the dumplings, pot and all.
"O why did you chase each other
And upset my pot of dumplings?"*

"*I'm not guilty; Mat is guilty.
He should not have pursued me so.*"
"'*Tis not my fault; Mary's guilty.
Her escape caused all this trouble.*"

187

93
W Murowanej Piwnicy
IN A CELLAR MADE OF BRICK

Con brio

W mu - ro - wa - nej   piw - ni - cy,   Tań - co - wa - li
In   a   cel - lar   made   of   brick,   Out- laws danced with

zbój - ni - cy.   Ko - za - li   se   pik - nie   grać
nim - ble   feet.   "Watch   our   feet,"   they   called   with   pride.

I   na   nós - ki   spo - zie - rać.   Hey! _____
"Play   your   best   there!"   they   called   out.   Hey! _____

Sung in 1940 by Adam Bartosz who learned the song in Poland.

W murowanej piwnicy	*In a cellar made of brick,*
Tańcowali zbójnicy.	*Outlaws[40] danced with nimble feet.*
Kozali se piknie grać	*"Watch our feet," they called with pride.*
I na nóski spozierać. Hej!	*"Play your best there!" they called out. Hey!*
Tańcowałbym kiebym móg,	*I would dance too, if I could,*
Kiebym ni mioł ksywych nóg.	*If my legs weren't badly bowed.*
Ale ksywe nóski mom,	*But alas! my legs are bowed.*
Co podskoce, to się gnom. Hej!	*When I leap they bend too much. Hey!*
Gonił zbójnik zbójnicke;	*Ho! An outlaw chased his lass*
Potorgoł jej spódnicke.	*And he tugged and pulled her skirt.*
A zbójnicka za nim, za nim,	*She ran after, after him,*
Potorgoła portki na nim. Hej!	*Till his breeches she did tear. Hey!*

94
Podkóweczki, Dajcie Ognia[41]
STEEL-TIPPED DANCE SHOES, FLASH AND SPARKLE

Pod - kó - wecz - ki daj - cie og - nia Bo dziew-
Steel - tipped dance shoes, flash and spar - kle, For this

czy - na te - go god - na. A czy god - na, czy nie
girl's a wor - thy part - ner. Be she wor - thy or not

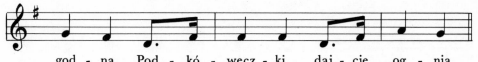

god - na, Pod - kó - wecz - ki, daj - cie og - nia.
wor - thy, Steel - tipped dance shoes, flash and spar - kle.

Sung in 1941 by Mrs. Ferdinand Chenik, who learned it from her mother.

Podkóweczki, dajcie ognia
Bo dziewczyna tego godna.
A czy godna, czy nie godna,
Podkóweczki, dajcie ognia.

Steel-tipped dance shoes, flash and sparkle,
For this girl's a worthy partner.
Be she worthy or not worthy,
Steel-tipped dance shoes, flash and sparkle.

95

Hop! Hop! Dziś, Dziś Za Kominem!

SEE THE MAZUR, HEY THE MAZUR!

Gaily

Hop! Hop! Dziś, dziś za ko - mi - nem Sie - dzi
See the Ma - zur, hey the Ma - zur! At the

Ma - zur ze swym sy - nem A Ma - zur - ka
fire - place with his fine son. See the young lass

ze swą cór - ką Za - glą - da - ją jed - ną
and her moth - er Sly - ly peek - ing through one

dziur - ką. A pa - ro - bek, to ci du - sza! Kej o -
key - hole. And the farm - hand, what a ras - cal! Left - ward

ber - ka w le - wo ru - sza. W pra - wo
swing - ing the o - be - rek. Right, then

le - wo ko - gu - ci - ka; Je - den
left he swings with vig - or. Ev - 'ry -

z dru - giem niech u - my - ka. La - la - la - la - la -
bod - y make room for him. La - la - la - la - la -

la, La - la - la - la - la - la - la - la - la - la,
la, La - la - la - la - la - la - la - la - la - la,

La - la - la - la - la - la - la - la - la,
La - la - la - la - la - la - la - la - la,

La - la - la - la - la - la - la - la.____
La - la - la - la - la - la - la - la.____

Sung in 1940 by Mrs. Alexandra Szczepanik, who learned it from her
mother in Poland.

Hop! Hop! Dziś, dziś za kominem
Siedzi Mazur ze swym synem.
A Mazurka ze swą córką
Zaglądają jedną dziurką.
A parobek to ci dusza!
Kej oberka w lewo rusza.
W prawo, lewo kogucika;
Jeden z drugiem niech umyka.

Refren:
La-la-la-la-la-la-la-la-la-la
La-la-la-la-la-la
La-la-la-la
La-la-la-la-la-la
La-la-la-la-la-la-la-la

See the Mazur, hey the Mazur!
At the fireplace with his fine son.
See the young lass and her mother
Slyly peeking through one keyhole.
And the farmhand, what a rascal!
Leftward swinging the oberek.
Right, then left he swings with vigor.
Ev'rybody make room for him.

Refrain:
La-la-la-la-la-la-la-la-la-la
La-la-la-la-la-la
La-la-la-la
La-la-la-la-la-la
La-la-la-la-la-la-la-la

V

The singer etches portraits of travelers who have been here and are gone or, being here, are going and will be no more except in song.

96
Siedzę Ja W Oknie
THROUGH THE WINDOWPANE

Con grazia

Sie - dzę ja w ok - nie Pa - trzę się szy - bą.
Through the win - dow - pane, What is this I see?

Mo - ja ma - mu - siu, Zło - dzie - ję i - dą. Mo - ja
O my dear Mam - ma, Out - laws are com - ing. O my

ma - mu - siu, Daj mi się u - brać Że - by ja się mo - gła
dear Mam - ma, May I wear my best, That I may be pleas - ing

Zło - dzie - jo - wi u - dać. Oj ra - chu cia - chu, Traj - la -
To a bold young out - law? O tra - la - la - la, Tra - la -

la - la - la, Oj ra - chu cia - chu, Traj - la - la - la - la.
la - la - la, O Tra - la - la - la, Tra - la - la - la - la.

Sung in 1941 by Mrs. Sophie Dziob, who learned it from friends in
Passaic, New Jersey.

194

Siedzę ja w oknie
Patrzę się szybą.
Moja mamusiu,
Złodzieję idą.
Moja mamusiu,
Daj mi się ubrać
Żeby ja się mogła
Złodziejowi udać.

Refren:
Oj rachu ciachu,
Traj - la - la - la,
Oj rachu chiachu,
Traj - la - la - la.

Bo na złodzieju
Ładne ubranie.
Spojrzysz na buty,
Lakierowane.
Bo na złodzieju
Bielutkie ręcę.
Spojrzysz na palce,
Złote pierścieńce.

Through the windowpane,
What is this I see?
O my dear Mamma,
Outlaws are coming.
O my dear Mamma,
May I wear my best,
That I may be pleasing
To a bold young outlaw?

Refrain:
O tra-la-la-la,
Tra la-la-la-la
O tra-la-la-la
Tra la-la-la-la.

What splendid clothing
Each bold outlaw wears.
Look at his fine boots,
Lustrous black leather.
Delicate white hands
Has each bold outlaw.
Look at his long fingers;
Rings of gold circle them.

97

Jedzie, Jedzie Rycerz Zbrojny[42]

AN ARMORED KNIGHT IS RETURNING

Moderato

Je - dzie, je - dzie ry - cerz zbroj - ny,
An ar - mored knight is re - turn - ing,

Co po - wra - ca z dłu - giej woj - ny,
Aft - er wag - ing man - y bat - tles,

Co po - wra - ca z dłu - giej woj - ny.
Aft - er wag - ing man - y bat - tles.

A ballad, sung in 1941 by Mrs. John Krupski, who learned it in Buffalo.

Jedzie, jedzie rycerz zbrojny,	*An armored knight is returning,*
Co powraca z długiej wojny,	*After waging many battles,*
Co powraca z długiej wojny.	*After waging many battles.*
Suknia jego zakrwawiona;	*Bloodstained are the garments on him;*
Szabla jego wyszczerbiona.	*Nicked and blunted is his fine sword.*
Przywitał go ojciec stary;	*His old father came to greet him;*
Siostry mu przyniosły dary.	*All his sisters brought him offerings.*
Bracia wszyscy go witali;	*And his brothers bid him welcome;*
Sąsiedzi się radowali.	*Neighbors gather to rejoice, too.*

"Matko moja, wyjdź z pokoju
I przywitaj syna z boju."

"Jakże może wyjść do ciebie,
Gdyż od roku po pogrzebie?"

"Wiecznie będę żył w żałobie,
Gdyż mateńka moja w grobie."

"*Mother dear, do leave your chamber;
Greet your son returned from battle.*"

"*How can she come out to greet you?
'Tis twelve months now since the fun'ral.*"

"*Always shall I live in mourning,
Since my mother lies in her grave.*"

98

Od Francyji Jadę

FROM FRANCE I COME TO YOU

(See number 101)

"Od Fran-cy - ji ja - dę, Sza - bel - kę nio-
"From France I come to you With my faih - ful

sę. Od Fran-cy - ji ja - dę, Sza - bel - kę nio-
sword. From France I come to you With my faith - ful

sę. Wyjdź - że mo - ja mi - ła, Wy - nieś
sword. Come forth, O my dar - ling, Bring my

mi chus - tecz - kę; O to cię pro - szę."
hand - ker - chief, dear. This I beg of you."

Sung in 1941 by Mrs. Sophia Dziob, who learned it from friends in
Passaic, New Jersey.

"Od Francyji jadę,
Szabelkę niosę.
Od Francyji jadę,
Szabelkę niosę.
Wyjdź-że moja miła,
Wynieś mi chusteczkę;
O to cię proszę."

"From France I come to you
With my faithful sword.
From France I come to you
With my faithful sword.
Come forth, O my darling,
Bring your handkerchief, dear.
This I beg of you."

"Ja ci nie wyniosę
Bom nie powinna.
Niech ci ją wyniesie
Twoja najmilejsza
Z Francyji inna.

"Boś ty po Francyji
Panny miłował;
A teraz odemnie,
I to nadaremnie,
Chusteczki żądasz."

"Nie było tam czasu
Panien miłować,
A bo tam kazali
Z rana do wieczora
Tak rycerować.

"A kto zna rycerkę
To mu jest dobrze.
Siędzi na koniku,
Podkręci wąsika,
Na wojne jedzie.

"Chcesz ma miła wiedzieć
Jakim napój miał?
Z pod kopyta konia
Woda wycieczona;
Takim napój miał.

"Chcesz ma miła wiedzieć
Jakim nocleg miał?
Trochę drzewa liścia,
Pod głowę tornistra;
Takim nocleg miał.

"Chcesz ma miła wiedzieć
Kto za mną płakał?
Tam na szczerem polu,
Tam na szczerem polu,
Czarny kruk krakał."

"*I'll not do your bidding;*
There's no reason to.
Get your handkerchief, man,
From the girl you loved so
While you were in France.

"*You have loved the French girls*
Over all the land;
Now you want my kerchief,
Though you have no reason
To ask it of me."

"*There was no time, darling,*
To love any girls,
For we were compelled to
Drill, maneuver daily,
Morn till dark of night.

"*He who knows his war games*
Is a lucky man.
His mustache he waxes,
Leaps upon his good horse,
Off to war he rides.

"*Would you know, my darling,*
What I had to drink?
Scooped-up muddy water,
Flooding ev'ry hoof print;
That I had to drink.

"*Would you know, my darling,*
Where I spent the night?
'Neath the leafy branches,
For my head a knapsack;
Thus I spent the night.

"*Would you know, my darling,*
Who wept o'er my plight?
In the barren pasture,
In the barren pasture,
Croaked a raven black."

99
Dawniej Dziadowie[43]
YEARS AGO BEGGARS

Andante

Daw-niej dzia-do-wie Miesz-ka-li w Kra-ko-wie; A głu-pi lud myś-lał Że a-pos-to-ło-wie. Daw-niej dziad każ-dy U-bie-rał się mod-nie; No-sił ak-sa-mit-ny sur-dut, I jed-wab-ne spod-nie. Raz się za-ko-cha-ła W dzia-

Years a-go, beg-gars lived in style in Kra-kow; Gul-li-ble folks be-lieved They were the A-pos-tles. Beg-gars in those days Sport-ed el-e-gant clothes. Their trou-sers were fash-ioned of silk, Vel-vet were their frock coats. A queen once fell in love With

dzie kró - lo - wa,   Aż   jej   zaz - droś - ci - ła   Ce -
one of these tramps; This love was cov - et - ed By

sa - rzo - wa   Jęd - rja - no - wa. ____
Em - press   A - dri - enne,   a - las! ____

Sung in 1940 by Mrs. Bernice Mochocka, who recalled a fragment
which she had learned in Dziektażewo, Poland.

Dawniej dziadowie	*Years ago, beggars*
Mieszkali w Krakowie,	*Lived in style in Krakow;*
A głupi lud myślał	*Gullible folks believed*
Że apostołowie.	*They were the apostles.*
Dawniej dziad każdy	*Beggars in those days*
Ubierał się modnie;	*Sported elegant clothes.*
Nosił aksamitny surdut,	*Their trousers were fashioned of silk,*
I jedwabne spodnie.	*Velvet were their frock coats.*
Raz się zakochała	*A queen once fell in love*
W dziadzie królowa,	*With one of the tramps;*
Aż jej zazdrościła	*This love was coveted*
Cesarzowa Jędrjanowa.	*By Empress Adrienne, alas!*

100

Jestem Dziodek z Łobzowa

I'M A BEGGAR FROM LOBZOW

Jes - tem dzio - dek z Łob - zo - wa, Nie da -
I'm a beg - gar from Lob - zow; Near - by

le - ko Kra - ko - wa. I mój łoj - ciec, mo - ja
Kra - kow I have lived. And my fath - er and my

mat - ka, I mój dzio - dek, mo - ja bab - ka Po od -
moth - er, And my grand - sire and my grand - dame, They were

pus - tach cho - dzi - li I to pieśń __ nu - ci -
pil - grims prais - ing God; And this song __ they did

li, O Ja - da - mie co beł w ra - ju, I ło
sing A - bout Ad - am's life in E - den, And a -

Świę - tym Mi - ko - ła - ju Co w pie - kle go - zoł.
bout St. Nich - o - las poor, He who burned in Hell.

Sung in 1940 by Mrs. Bernice Mochocka, who learned it from a
wandering beggar in Dziektażewo, Poland.

Jestem dziodek z Łobzowa,	*I'm a beggar from Lobzow;*
Nie daleko Krakowa.	*Nearby Krakow I have lived.*
I mój łojciec, moja matka,	*And my father and my mother,*
I mój dziodek, moja babka	*And my grandsire and my grandame,*
Po odpustach chodzili	*They were pilgrims praising God;*
I to pieśń nucili,	*And this song they did sing*
O Jadamie co beł w raju,	*About Adam's life in Eden,*
I ło Swiętem Mikołaju	*And about St Nicholas poor,*
Co w piekle gozoł.	*He who burned in Hell.*

101

Na Krakowskiem Zamku

NEAR A KRAKOW CASTLE

(Variant of number 98)

Con brio

"Na Kra - kow - skiem zam - ku, Sto - i
"Near a Kra - kow cas - tle, Stands a

czar - ny koń. Któż na niem po -
coal black horse. Who will be its

je - dzie? Któż na niem po - je dzie?
rid - er? Who will be its rid - er?

1 Sta - sio lu - by mój." **2** Sta sio lu - by mój."
My be - lov - ed Stan." My be - lov - ed Stan."

Sung in 1941 by Frank First, who learned it from a friend,
who had learned it in Poland while serving in World War I.

204

"Na Krakowskiem zamku,
Stoi czarny koń.
Na Krakowskiem zamku,
Stoi czarny koń.
Któż na niem pojedzie?
Któż na niem pojedzie?
Stasio luby mój.
Któż na niem pojedzie?
Któż na niem pojedzie?
Stasio luby mój."

"Od Francyji jadę,
Szabelką toczę.
Wynieś mi ma miła,
Wynieś mi chusteczkę.
Oto cię proszę."

"Ja ci nie wyniosę,
Bom nie powinna.
Niech ci ją wyniesie,
Niech ci ją wyniesie
Z Francyji inna.

"Boś ty po Francyji
Panny miłował;
Teraz byś odemnie,
Lecz to na daremnie,
Chusteckę żądał."

"Nie było tam czasu
Panny miłować,
Boś my tam musieli,
Boś my tam musieli,
Egzecyrować.

"Kto egzecyrkie zna,
Temu jest dobrze.
Siada na konika,
Podkręci wąsika,
Na wojne jedzie.

"Chcesz ma miła wiedzieć
Jaki obiad mój?
Kawał mięsa z konia,
Pod siodłem pieczona;
Taki obiad mój.

"Near a Krakow castle,
Stands a coal black horse.
Near a Krakow castle,
Stands a coal black horse.
Who will be its rider?
Who will be its rider?
My belovèd Stan.
Who will be its rider?
Who will be its rider?
My belovèd Stan."

"I'm returning from France
With my faithful sword.
Come forth, O my darling,
Bring your handkerchief, dear;
This I beg of you."

"I'll not do your bidding;
There's no reason to.
Let another do it,
Let another do it,
One you've loved in France.

"You have loved the French girls
Over all the land,
Now you want my kerchief,
Though you have no reason
To ask it of me."

"There was no time, darling,
To love any girls,
For we were compelled to,
For we were compelled to
Drill and drill and drill.

"He who knows his war games
Is a lucky man.
His mustache he waxes,
Leaps upon his good horse;
Off to war he rides.

"Would you know, my darling,
What my dinner was?
Chunks of horsemeat roasted
'Neath the rider's saddle;
Thus I dined each night.

"Chcesz ma miła wiedzieć
Jaki napój mój?
Z pod kopyta konia
Woda wygnieciona;
Taki napój mój.

"Chcesz ma miła wiedzieć
Jaka śmierć moja?
Kula rozpalona,
W sercu mem utkwiona;
Taka śmierć moja."

"*Would you know, my darling,
What I had to drink?
Scooped-up muddy water,
Flooding ev'ry hoof print;
That I had to drink.*

"*Would you know, my darling,
What my fate will be?
Fire-fed sizzling bullets,
Lodged within my heart;
Such will be my fate.*"

VI

Sometimes people sing for the joy of singing, caring not where they begin or stop or what they sing.

102

Od Krakowa Czarny Las

FORESTS BLACK NEAR KRAKOW GROW

Allegretto

Od Kra-ko-wa czar-ny las, Od Kra-ko-wa czar-ny las. Py-ta-ła się Ka-sia O swo-je-go Ja-sia, Czy po-wró-ci z woj-ny,— Czy po-wró-ci z woj-ny, w czas?

For-ests black near Kra-kow grow, For-ests black near Kra-kow grow. Ka-tie asked a-bout her Much be-lov-ed John-ny, Would he come home from war,— Would he come home from war soon?

Sung in 1940 by Mrs. Alexandra Szczepanik, who learned it in Bircze, Poland.

Od Krakowa czarny las,	*Forests black near Krakow grow,*
Od Krakowa czarny las.	*Forests black near Krakow grow.*
Pytała się Kasia	*Katie asked about her*
O swojego Jasia,	*Much beloved Johnny,*
Czy powróci z wojny,	*Would he come home from war,*
Czy powróci z wojny wczas?	*Would he come home from war soon?*

"Oj wywija chusteczką
Oj od szczerego złota,
Co ja mu ją dała,
Co ja mu ją dała,
Oj uboga sierota,
Oj uboga sierota."

"Oj cobyśty była
Oj uboga sierota,
Nie dawała byśty,
Nie dawała byśty
Oj chusteczek od złota,
Oj chusteczek od złota."

Miałeś chamie czapkie z piór,
Miałeś chamie złoty róg,
Czapkę wicher niesie,
Róg huczy po lesie,
Ostał ci się jeno sznur,
Ostał ci się jeno sznur.

"O he waves his handkerchief,
O his golden handkerchief,
One that I have giv'n him,
One that I have giv'n him,
O the orphan that I am,
O the orphan that I am."

"O were you an orphan poor,
O an orphan very poor,
Never would you give me,
Never would you give me
O a kerchief of pure gold,
O a kerchief of pure gold."

Churl, you owned a feathered cap,[44]
Churl, you owned a golden horn,
Now your horn is wind-born;
Through the woods your horn blares;
All that's left you is a rope,
All that's left you is a rope.

103

Żebym Ja Tak Miała[45]

HOW I WISH I COULD HAVE

Że - bym ja tak mia - ła Skrzy - deł -
How I wish I could have Fleet wings

ka jak gąs - ka; Po - le - cia - ła -
of a gos - ling. Swift - ly would I

bym ja, Po - le - cia - ła - bym ja
fly to, Swift - ly would I fly to

Za Ja - siem do Śląz - ka. Śląz - ka. _____
John - ny in Si - le - sia. le - sia. _____

Sung in 1941 by Frank First, who learned it from a friend in
Pennsylvania.

Żebym ja tak miała
Skrzydełka jak gąska,
Żebym ja tak miała
Skrzydełka jak gąska,
Poleciałabym ja,
Poleciałabym ja
Za Jasiem do Śląska.
Poleciałabym ja,
Poleciałabym ja
Za Jasiem do Śląska.

I usiadłabym se
W tym Śląsku na płocie;
Przypatrzyłabym się,
Przypatrzyłabym się
Jasiowej robocie.

Jak oni tam piją
I w talary grają,
A ich biedne żonki,
A ich biedne żonki
Z głodu umierają.

Piszą do nich listy
Choć po jeden złoty,
Oni odpisują,
Oni odpisują,
"Nie mamy roboty.

"Roboty nie mamy;
Co dzień jej szukamy.
Te Pitzburskie majny,
Te Pitzburskie majny
Często odwiedzamy."

How I wish I could have
Fleet wings of a gosling;
How I wish I could have
Fleet wings of a gosling.
Swiftly would I fly to,
Swiftly would I fly to
Johnny in Silesia.
Swiftly would I fly to,
Swiftly would I fly to
Johnny in Silesia.

And I would alight on
A fence in Silesia,
And I would survey there,
And I would survey there
All of Johnny's labor.

I would watch them drinking,
Playing cards and gambling,
While their wretched spouses,
While their wretched spouses
Were of hunger dying.

When they write them letters
For at least one zloty,
Always they do answer,
Always they do answer,
"We have no employment.

"We have no employment;
Daily do we search it;
And those Pittsburgh coal mines,
And those Pittsburgh coal mines
Often we do visit."

104

Na Dolinie Zawierucha[46]

WHIRLWINDS RAGING IN THE VALLEY

Allegretto

Na do - li - nie za - wie - ru - cha,
Whirl - winds rag - ing in the val - ley,

Wiatr ze śnie - giem dmie;
Mad - ly swirl - ing snow;

A w ko - mi - nie
In the chim - ney

o - gień bu - cha, Trzas - ka w ko - ło
flames are leap - ing, Crack - ling all a -

mnie. A w ko - mi - nie. o - gień
round. In the chim - ney flames are

bu - cha, Trzas - ka w ko - ło mnie.
leap - ing, Crack - ling all a - round.

Sung in 1940 by Mrs. John Krupski, who learned it from a friend
in Buffalo.

Na dolinie zawierucha,
Wiatr ze śniegiem dmie;
A w kominie ogień bucha,
Trzaska w koło mnie.
A w kominie ogień bucha,
Trzaska w koło mnie.

Whirlwinds raging in the valley,
Madly swirling snow;
In the chimney flames are leaping,
Crackling all around.
In the chimney flames are leaping,
Crackling all around.

105

Ej! Tyś Moja, Dziewczyno
HO! NOW YOU ARE MINE, DEAR GIRL

Con brio

Ej! tyś mo - ja, dziew - czy - no;
Ho! now you are mine, dear — girl;

Ej! tyś mo - ja, tyś mo - ja.
Ho! you are mine, yes you — are.

Ej! ja cię wy - pro - wa - dził
Ho! how gen - tly I led you

Ej! za rącz - kę z koś - cio - ła.
Ho! from church by your fair — hand.

Sung in 1941 by Frank First, who learned it from a friend in
Pennsylvania.

Ej! tyś moja, dziewczyno;	"*Ho! now you are mine, dear girl;*
Ej! tyś moja, tyś moja.	*Ho! you are mine, yes you are.*
Ej! ja cię wyprowadził	*Ho! how gently I led you*
Ej! za rączkę z kościoła.	*Ho! from church by your fair hand.*
Ej! ja cię wyprowadził	*Ho! how gently I led you*
Ej! za rączkę z kościoła.	*Ho! from church by your fair hand.*

Ej! za rączkę z kościoła,
Ej! za rączkę do domu.
A dziewczyno tyś moja.
Ej! nie dam cię nikomu.

Ej! na Soniskiem polu,
Ej! na Soniskiej drodze,
Sznuruje se dziewczyna
Ej! buciki na drodze.

Ej! sznuruje, sznuruje
Ej! jedwabną wstążeczką,
A oczki zapłakane,
Ej! wyciera chusteczką.

Ej! szumiała leszczyna
A jakiem przez nią jechał.
Ej! płakała dziewczyna
Ej! żem nią tak pogardził.

Ej! iżeś mną pogardził,
Ja i tak będę żyła.
Ej! a ciebie chultaju
Ej! będzie bieda biła.

"Ho! from church by your fair hand,
Ho! right home by your fair hand.
Yes, dear girl, now you are mine.
Ho! I'll never give you up.

"Ho! in a Sonisk meadow,
Ho! upon a Sonisk road,
There I saw a girl lacing
Ho! her shoes right on the road.

"Ho! thus lacing, yes lacing
Ho! with ribbon of true silk,
And her eyes, reddened with tears,
Ho! she dried with her kerchief.

"Ho! the hazel grove rustled
As through it I came riding;
Ho! the girl was weeping there
Because I cared naught for her."

"Ho! though you care naught for me,
Life will go on just the same,
Ho! but you will e'er be scourged
Ho! by poverty, you wretch."

AN ANALYSIS OF THE POLISH FOLKSONGS

by Grace L. Engel

AN ANALYSIS OF THE POLISH FOLKSONGS

by Grace L. Engel

It has become increasingly apparent to students of folklore in the United States in recent years that if folksong is to be studied accurately, the melody must not be neglected but must assume equal importance with the text. The work of George Herzog, Phillips Barry, and Cecil Sharp indicates the increasing value placed upon the preservation and analysis of melody as well as text. In the opinion of the authors of *British Ballads from Maine* "the student of folksong..., who has only the texts to work with, is placed at a serious disadvantage in so far as he is out of touch with the folksong as living song."[1] Realizing the validity of this point of view, Miss Harriet Pawlowska has recorded the melodies for her collection of Polish folksongs on the dictagraph. It has been my privilege to transcribe them.

Polish musicians residing on foreign soil have always kept the music of Poland free from the influence of other nationalities. Chopin and Paderewski, both cosmopolitans, perpetuated the intense nationalism of Polish music in their compositions. The folk have done likewise. Polish immigrants in the United States have tenaciously preserved their folksongs, a living link with their homeland.

The 105 folksongs which comprise Miss Pawlowska's collection, coming from the hearts of Polish singers, are an index of the emotional, social, and spiritual life of the people of Poland, truly revealing their temperament, customs, observances, and beliefs. It is the temperament of the Polish people to be happy and joyous. They use song as a means of uplift to forget their worries and burdens. In the fields, the peasants sing, thus forgetting their fatigue and the monotony of their labor.

Polish folksongs are truly a form of art, expressing the emotional qualities of love, joy, sadness, courage, and peace. Both by tangible and intangible means are emotional qualities expressed in music. Never will it be possible to transcribe a folksong in its entirety. Only the tangible elements of the song, namely, rhythm, melody, and structure, can be recorded by this means. There will always be the intangible element of "interpretation," which will elude the pencil and paper of the collector.

Every folk singer considers the song he is singing to be his own individual property. To quote Percy Grainger, "He unhesitatingly alters the traditional material he has inherited... to suit his own voice or instrument, or to make it conform to his purely personal taste for rhythm and general style."[2]

To the song the singer lends certain subtleties of interpretation and expression, which cannot be recorded on paper. Imperceptible pauses, subtle quarter-tone or eighth-tone variations in pitch, slight changes in note value not great enough to change rhythmic notation, often occasioned by the meaning or spirit of the text—all these factors comprise the true essence of folksong. Another intangible factor of great importance is *tempo rubato*,[3] which characterizes not only Polish folk music but art music as well. Paderewski said of his native music, "Change follows change almost without transition, from blissful rapture to sobbing woe.... Our land, the whole of Poland lives, feels, and moves in *tempo rubato*."[4]

There is only one way by which these intangible elements can be captured, the recording machine. Concerning this method, Alan and John Lomax say:

The needle writes on the disc with tireless accuracy the subtle inflections, the melodies, the pauses that comprise the emotional meaning of speech, spoken and sung. In this way folklore can truly be recorded.[5]

Despite the limitations of notation, careful attention to tempo marks and expression marks will reveal, to some extent, the manner in which the songs of the present collection are to be sung.

In terms of the tangible factors of rhythm, melody, and structure, an analysis and a comparison of the songs reveal many characteristics which they have in common. Several songs, or portions of songs, are essentially the same, with slight melodic and rhythmic differences. The beginning phrases of songs 15 and 8 are similar, as are the beginning phrases of songs 2 and 57. Song 94 is a fragment of song 95. Songs 43 and 5 have basically the same text as well as essentially the same melody. Songs 39 and 55, sung by the same singer, are excellent examples of melodic transference.

"The foundation of Polish music is the Polish folksong of a richness and rhythmical variety that cannot be met with elsewhere."[6] Thus spoke one of Poland's foremost musical sons, Artur Rodzinski. Rhythmically, the songs here are divided into two groups: 70 percent can be listed as rhythmically regular; 30 percent irregular. The first term denotes a song which possesses rhythmic continuity and the same meter signature throughout. The irregular song is one which changes the meter signature within the song.

The group which is regular may be analyzed as follows:

Classification	Meter Signature		Percentage
Simple Triple Time	3/4		28
Simple Duple Time	2/4	(a) 28	
	4/4	(b) 9	37
Compound Duple Time	6/8	(a) 4	
	6/4	(b) 1	5

The songs which are rhythmically irregular are indeed songs which elude metrical discipline. Four rhythmic alterations, for the most part, are responsible for changes in meter signature. These are as follows:

1. The change may be due to an added beat which often occurs at the end of a phrase. (Songs 7, 30, 43, 57, 67.) Rhythmic change may be due, also, to the absence of a beat. (Songs 17, 24, 74, 82, 90.)

2. The alteration may occur to accommodate extra syllables in the words of the text. (Songs 28, 92.)

3. A rhythmic contraction may exist. A half note (♩) may become a quarter note (♩). Two quarter notes (♩ ♩) may become two eighth notes (♫). (Songs 14, 95.)

4. A rhythmic expansion may occur. A dotted eighth note followed by a sixteenth note (♪.♪) may become a dotted quarter note followed by an eighth note (♩.♪). (Song 73.)

Some changes in meter signature can be explained only in terms of the nature of the folk singer and the complete freedom with which he sings his songs. (Songs 20, 27, 86, 92.)

Folksong is "song alive, a living organism, subject to all the conditions and manifesting all the phenomena of growth and change."[7] In no way do these metrical changes detract from the artistic value of the songs. Rather, because of the rhythmic agreement of the text and the music, these changes are achieved smoothly, the song becoming an organic whole. (See song 42.) Rhythmic diversity is one of the outstanding characteristics of the Polish folksong, equalled only by the folksongs of Russia.[8]

Various uses of one rhythmic pattern occur again and again in this collection. It is the rhythmic figure of a dotted eighth note followed by a sixteenth note (♪.♬), which occurs in thirty-four of the songs. The most common uses are in the following patterns:

(a) 3/4 ♪.♬ | ♩ ♩ ♩ |

(b) 3/4 ♪.♬ ♩ ♩ |

(c) 2/4 ♪.♬ ♬ |

The use of these patterns is undoubtedly due to the influence of the Polish dances: (a) the *mazurka*, a national dance of stately character with varied accents, and (b) the *oberek*, which is very popular and achieves its greatest vigor in the south of Poland. (Songs 46, 49, 95.) The rhythmic patterns of these two dances are:

(a) *mazurka:* | 3/4 ♪.♬ ♩ ♩ | ♪.♬ ♩ ♩ |

(b) *oberek:* | 3/4 ♪.♬ | ♩ ♩ ♪.♬ | ♩ ♩ ♪.♬ |

Four songs show the influence of the gay and sprightly *krakowiak*, which is full of syncopation and unexpected accent. (Songs 29, 39, 53, 55.) Its rhythmic pattern is short:

| 2/4 ♪ ♩̄ ♪ |

Melodically, the folksongs are exquisite. (See songs 2, 6, 17, 33, 65, 69.) They are, for the most part, based on the tonic, subdominant, and dominant harmony of the major and minor modes. Analyzed as to mode, we find:

77 percent of the songs are in the major mode,

15 percent of the songs are in the minor mode,

8 percent modulate from major to minor and vice versa.

One song only conforms to an ancient Greek modal pattern. It is number 83, which is based upon the ancient Greek Hypo-Dorian mode. Careful analysis of the melodic line will indicate that it is not the minor mode as we know it today. With "a" as the keynote, we discover that two scale steps resolve unnaturally: "3" resolves to "7" and "6" resolves to "7."

In a sense, it may be said that all the songs are modal, for the major and minor modes which have controlled the composition of Occidental music for hundreds of years are two of nine Greek modes; namely, the Lydian and the Hypo-Dorian. With the exception of song 83, very seldom is the listener aware of any unnatural melodic resolutions. The active scale steps resolve normally to their rest tones: 2 to 1, 4 to 3, 6 to 5 and 7 to 8.

The beginning and ending tones of the songs are predominantly conventional. Seventy-seven percent of the songs begin on the first, third, or fifth scale steps, with a definite feeling for tonic harmony. Nineteen percent begin on the fifth scale step, with a definite feeling for dominant harmony. Four percent begin on the lowered sixth scale step, or second scale step.

Ninety-four percent have a tonic ending, with the majority ending on the first scale step, a few on the third. Six percent end on the fifth scale step, with a feeling for dominant harmony. This type of ending indicates a circular song, a song of many verses in which the same melody is repeated many times.

Melodic figures are often chordal in nature; that is, the melodic sequence of one or two measures belongs to one chord. (See songs 8, 13, 15, 25, 35.) In general, the songs derive their melodic structure from the tonic, subdominant, and dominant chords of the key.

Modulation is relatively rare, occurring in only fourteen of the songs. Analysis of modulation is as follows:

1. Tonic minor to tonic major. (See songs 27, 71, 84.)
2. Major to relative minor. (See song 92.)
3. Minor to relative major. (See songs 88, 91.)
4. Next related keys. (See songs 14, 18, 29, 41, 44, 48, 76.)

The range of the Polish folk melodies is interesting:

	Percent
Octave and a sixth	1
Octave and a fourth	4
Tenth or eleventh	4
Octave or ninth	69
Seventh	11
Fifth or sixth	10
Fourth	1

I once heard Percy Grainger say that the range of a song is determined by the circumstances of its composition. A shepherd singing upon the hillside will compose a song of wide range to suit his own voice. On the other hand, a song composed for a group will have a limited range. The Polish folk, primarily an agricultural group, work alone in the fields. The wide range of an octave, ninth, or more, as exhibited in their songs, would thus substantiate Grainger's statement.

The last, but not the least, of the three tangible elements of folk music is structure.

> Folk song is the smallest possible form as well as the simplest, to which one may still rightfully apply the term 'work of art'. Condensed in size, though it is, it is not fragmentary but a miniature, complete and symmetrically finished....[9]

There is an interesting agreement between the rhythmic characteristics of the songs and their form. Fifty-one are of regular construction, fifty-four of irregular construction. We may define a song of regular construction as one having good balance, achieved by an equal number of phrases, each of which is of consistent length.

The most common unit of the fifty-one regular songs is the two-measure phrase. In this group, twelve are composed of four phrases, the regular double period form; ten are composed of six phrases, three songs have eight phrases, four have two, three, five, and nine phrases, respectively. Seventeen songs consist of four-measure phrases. Six of these have four phrases, eight have six phrases, two have three phrases, and one has five phrases. Four songs have three-measure phrases, of which three have six phrases, and one is four phrases in length. One song consists of four one-measure phrases.

The songs which must be classified as structurally irregular are those possessing the most rhythmical diversity. They can be analyzed as being free in style and yet possessing melodic and rhythmic unity.

Many of the songs indicate a perfection of structure similar to the art songs of the great masters. (See songs 4, 6, 10, 64, 65.)

The term "form," as defined by Percy Goetschius, applies to the majority of the songs in the present collection. Mr. Goetschius states:

> A musical composition, then, in which order prevails; in which all the factors are chosen and treated in close keeping with their logical bearing upon each other and upon the whole; in which, in a word, there is no disorder of thought or technique,—is music with form (i.e., good form).[10]

Evident in the songs of the present collection are the elements of unity and variety, which when "sensibly matched and evenly balanced" contribute to good form.[11]

After my analysis of the rhythmic, melodic, and structural characteristics of these songs I must acknowledge that what Phillips Barry says of British folksongs is equally true of Polish folksongs:

> ... in its melodic content and technical structure, the music will reveal the conservatism and good artistic judgment of the singers. By far the larger part of the folk music... will be a monument to the critical discrimination and good taste of the singers who have transmitted it.[12]

NOTES

NOTES TO THE SONGS

[1] According to Francis James Child, the ballad about the maid who poisoned her brother is the Polish version of "Lord Randal" (Child, No. 12). For comparative notes, see Francis James Child, *The English and Scottish Popular Ballads*, I, 151-166; H. M. Belden, *Ballads and Songs Collected by the Missouri Folklore Society*, 24-28; Emelyn Elizabeth Gardner and G. J. Chickering, *Ballads and Songs of Southern Michigan*, 35-36. For Polish variants, see Oskar Kolberg, *Lud*, IV, Part 2, 49; VI, Part 2, 176-177; XVI, Part 1, 291; XIX, Part 2, 150; *Mazowsze*, II, Part 2, 106; Jan Sembrzycki, "Przyczyniki do Charakterystyki Mazurów Pruskich," *Wisła*, III, 584-585.

[2] The wreath is a symbol of chastity among the Polish folk. It is customary for peasant girls to wear garlands in their hair during festive occasions. The wedding wreath of rosemary or rue is removed during an important ceremony on the wedding day, and replaced with a matron's cap. For a further discussion, see Zygmunt Gloger, *Encyklopedja Staropolska*, IV, 430-432.

[3] A version collected by Kolberg in the Mazovian District presents an interesting array of farm animals and fowl who give their reactions to the second wife:

Była baba z Torunia,	*There was an old woman of Thorn*
Była baba, edziu, bedziu,	*There was an old woman, eejoo, beejoo,*
Dyłu, dyłu, dyłu, z Torunia.	*Dilloo, dilloo, dilloo of Thorn.*
. . . .	. . . .
Celadka będzie mówiła,	*The servants will say,*
"Lepij nieboska rządziła."	*"The former mistress ruled more wisely."*
Komornica będzie gadała,	*The tenant will say,*
"Prędzy nieboska co dała."	*"The former mistress was generous."*
I wółki będą rycały,	*And the little oxen will moo,*
"Więcy my cego dostały."	*"We were well fed in those days."*
I krówki będą rycały.	*And the little cows will moo*
Ze w pokładeckach jadały.	*That they were fed in troughs.*
I gęsi będą gęgały,	*And the geese will honk,*
I kóry będą gdakały,	*And the chickens will cackle*
I świnie będą kwicały	*And the pigs will squeel that*
Ze za nieboskie jadały.	*They had been fed in those days.*
I dziatki będą płakały,	*And the children will cry,*
"Lepsą my piersą mać miały."	*"Our first mother was much better."*
Kupcie se dzieci kokoszkę;	*"Children, buy yourselves a cackling hen;*
Niech wam wyzebie nieboskę.	*Let it disinter you dead mother."*
Nic juz nie nada kokoska	*"Useless is a cackling hen,*
Kiej juz nie zyje nieboska.	*For our poor mother is dead."*

In contrast to the plant burden used in the Detroit version, the Mazovian song begins with a strange incantation of Polish nonsense syllables. Charles Lowry Wimberly, *Folklore in the English and Scottish Ballads*, states that burdens which seem to be corruptions of Latin exorcisms are often found in old songs. See Wimberly, 351, for further discussion of Latin magic formulas. For the complete text and music of the above song, see Kolberg, *Mazowsze*, II, Part 2, 22. For variants, see Kolberg, *Lud*, I, 128; XII, Part 4, 21; Zygmunt Gloger, *Pieśni Dawne*, 43.

[4] In a twenty-two stanza version collected in the Province of Krakow, recorded in the peasant dialect, the suitor sings: "There is nothing wrong with me; I am young and energetic. My cheeks are like apples; my mustache is handsome. The pocket in my jacket is empty, but that is not important, for my fists are strong and my hands are made for work. As for him, he is a homely one, but he owns a cottage and he has a herd of cattle and fields and a pile of money. Foolish girl! To be so attracted to riches that she should prefer that simpleton to me. What is money without love, foolish Katie?

"Weak persuasion is of little use, for you can put out the sun before you can convince a woman. I will join the army and become a general. I will have a crested staff, and a bag of money stuffed like a sausage. I will ride through the village on my horse, and soldiers without number will follow me. I will drag John out of his cottage and beat him. 'Leave Katie alone!' I will cry. Then Katie will want me, but I will be angry—at first. Later I will soften. I will buy land and build for Katie. I will till the soil and the Lord will help me, for He will put strength into my shoulders and might into my fists. John will be my swineherd. Let him watch my good fortune, for Katie and I will love each other eternally, and when the Lord bestows children upon us, they will be as handsome as we are." See Kolberg, *Lud*, VI, Part 2, 299-300.

[5] For variants, see Kolberg, *Lud*, IV, Part 2, 67; VI, Part 2, 185-186; *Mazowsze*, II, Part 2, 111-112.

[6] In the opinion of Professor Child, this is the Polish version of "The Twa Magicians" (Child No. 44). Child, *The English and Scottish Popular Ballads*, I, 401. For variants collected in Poland, see Kolberg, *Lud* I, 134; IV, Part 2, 19; VI, Part 2, 129-130; *Mazowsze*, II, Part 2, 54-56.

[7] Wladyslaw Ludwik Anczyc (1823-1883), poet and playwright, uses this song in a one-act comic opera, *Łobzowianie*. Kolberg collected this song in Krakow Province in 1873, in Posen Province in 1879, and in Mazovia in 1886. For variants, see Kolberg, *Lud*, VI, Part 2, 145-146; XII, Part 4, 123; *Mazowsze*, II, Part 2, 260.

[8] Kolberg cites songs with similar endings which were used by matchmakers during the unveiling of the bride. See Kolberg, *Lud*, III, Part I, 272, 302-303. For variants, see Kolberg, *Lud*, XII, Part 4, 84; *Mazowsze*, II, Part I, 69.

[9] For variants, see Kolberg, *Lud*, I, 139; VI, Part 2, 150; *Mazowsze*, II, Part 2, 58-59.

[10] For variants, see Kolberg, Lud, XII, Part 4, 159-161.

[11] The cuckoo has been recognized generally as a harbinger of spring and fertility. As such it is closely associated with the fortunes of lovers, and the prognostication of their future. See Charles Swainson, *The Folk Lore and Provincial Names of British Birds*, 109-122.

[12] This song enjoys popularity among the Slavic people in general and the Polish people in particular. Bystroń wrote of it, "Possibly the greatest popularity is enjoyed by the sentimental song about the lovers, one of whom will blossom like a red rose and the other like a guelder rose." Jan Stanisław Bystroń, *Pieśni Ludu Polskiego*, 46-47, 146-147.

[13] Adam Mickiewicz, Polish poet (1798-1855), referred to this song in the epilog to his *Pan Tadeusz* when he wrote that he hoped his book would find its way beneath thatched roofs where village maidens could sing its songs as easily and readily as they sang their own folksong

"Of that orphan fair as dawn, who tried
Homeward to drive the geese at eventide."

See Oliver Elton, "Epilogue to Pan Tadeusz," *Slavonic and East European Review*, XIX (1939-40), 1-13 (*Slavonic Yearbook*, VI). For a variant collected in Posen Province, see Kolberg, *Lud*, XIII, Part 5, 51.

[14]   This song has often been used in Christmas puppet shows (*szopki*) in Poland. According to Kolberg, St. Francis of Assisi used puppets to depict scenes from the life of Christ. Eventually, these performances spread to churches throughout Europe. In Warsaw, when these became too worldly, Bishop Czartoryski issued an edict in 1711 prohibiting their presentation in places of worship. Other bishops followed suit, and the *szopki* became secular in nature. The first puppet shows to travel through the streets of Warsaw appeared in 1701. Like the original church presentations, these too had a decidedly religious character, but slowly they acquired a worldly flavor, often imitating scenes from the theater. A typical puppet show of that period began with the singing of Christmas carols. These were followed with scenes from the life of the community, which included the appearance of the chimney sweep, the highlander, the Cracovian and his Cracovienne, a wedding party, a sailor, a German, a Frenchman, an Hungarian, a Mazovian and his dancers, a Cossack, a soldier and his dancing Margaret, and finally Herod and the devil. As each puppet appeared, a typical scene was enacted accompanied by a song. After the performance, a beggar in a monk's hood, walked among the audience and asked for alms for the players. For further discussion of this subject, see Kolberg, *Mazowsze*, I, Part 1, 75-78. For variants of the song, see Kolberg, *Lud*, IV, Part 2, 61; *Mazowsze*, I, Part 1, 86; Zygmunt Gloger, *Zwyczaje i Pieśni Doroczne*, 23.

[15]   For variants, see Kolberg, *Lud*, IV, Part 2, 47-48; *Mazowsze*, II, Part 2, 94-95; IV, 311-313.

[16]   According to the singer, the patrol took the boy because he had gone beyond the limits of his own village and therefore was subject to arrest and army service.

[17]   For variants, see Kolberg, *Lud*, XIII, Part 5, 53-55.

[18]   Giewont is a mountain peak in the Tatra Mountains of southwestern Poland.

[19]   For variants, see Kolberg, *Lud*, IV, Part 2, 27; XII, Part 4, 131-134.

[20]   Comic songs dealing with the wedding of beasts, animals at work, etc., were known generally throughout western and southern Europe and were diffused throughout Poland by wandering minstrels. For variants, see Bystroń, *Pieśni Ludu Polskiego*, 52-55; Kolberg, *Mazowsze*, II, Part 2, 155, 308.

[21]   Adam Mickiewicz referred to this song in the epilog to *Pan Tadeusz:*

> "The village maids who turn
> Their wheels will chant the songs they love to learn,
> Songs of that tuneful girl who could not cease
> To strum on her dear fiddle and lost her geese."

See Elton, "Epilogue to Pan Tadeusz," *Slavonic Yearbook*, VI, 4.

[22]   For a discussion of this hunting song, widely known in Poland, see Bystroń, *Pieśni Ludu Polskiego*, 70-71. For variants, see Kolberg, *Lud*, VI, Part 2, 210-211; XII, Part 4, 266; *Mazowsze*, II, Part 2, 129; III, 295.

[23]   For variants, see Kolberg, *Lud*, XIII, Part 5, 4, 5.

[24]   For variants collected in Poland, see Kolberg, *Lud*, IV, Part 2, 22-23; XVIII, Part 1, 152.

[25]   For other ballads, see numbers 2, 38, and 97.

[26]   If we accept the theory that folksongs originated among people of the upper social order and gradually found their way to the masses, where they were modified and accepted, this song may give an interesting clue. In a version cited by Gloger (*Pieśni Dawne*, 11) which begins like *Tam Poza Góry*, one finds the vestiges of feudal Poland:

"Dam ci chusteczki;
Owiń nóżeczki;
Pojedziemy w obce kraje,
Gdzie są inne obyczaje;
Malowany dom.

Malowany dom,
Baszty ze wszech stron;
Mosty, baszty, złote sale,
Wszystko tam jest tak wspaniałe,
Jak u rycerza."

Przez wieś jechali;
Ludzie pytali,
"Co to, co to za dziewczyna?
Co to co to za jedyna
Jedzie z panami?"

Oj jedzie, jedzie
Na złotym rzędzie;
Sto par koni idzie za nią
Jak za jaką wielką panią
Z wielką paradą.

Z wielką paradą
Po moście jadą;
Trąbią po górach trębacze;
Zwożą swej pani haracze
Wierni poddani.

Wierni poddani
Przynieśli w dani
Dary wielkie, dary małe;
A jegomość serce stałe
Przyniósł w ofierze.

Przyniósł w ofierze;
A więc rycerze!
Każdy niech uradowany
Rozpocznie wesołe tany;
Naprzód polskiego!

"I shall give you handkerchiefs.
Wrap your little feet.
We shall ride to distant places
Where the customs are not like ours.
Mansions which defy description.

"Mansions which defy description,
With bastions on all sides.
Bridges, bastions, halls of gold.
Everything with splendor filled,
As befits a knight."

They rode through the village,
And the people asked,
"Who is, who is that fair maiden?
Who is she of so great fortune,
Riding with the gentlemen?"

O she rides and rides
In a golden file.
With a hundred pairs of horses
Riding after this fair lady
In a grand parade.

In a grand parade
They ride o'er the bridge.
Trumpets sound from all the heights,
Faithful vassals meet their lady,
Laden with tribute.

Faithful vassals
Bring her gifts,
Lay before her large and small gifts,
While his lordship, faithful ever,
Offers her his heart.

Offers her his heart;
Therefore, gallant knights,
Rejoice on this day,
Start the merry dance,
Poland's national dance!

In the following version (*Mazowsze*, III, 132) the Mazovians substitute wagons, wreaths, and rings of silver for the splendor of the Middle Ages. The first three stanzas are similar to those of the song in this collection. The song continues:

"A wy woźnice, smarujcie bice
A wy woźnice, smarujcie bice
I te wozy wytacajcie
I te koniki zaprzęgajcie
Pojedziemy precz."

Przez wieś jechali,
Przez wieś jechali;
Ludzie patrzali;
"A coz to ta za panowie
Panne porwali?"

"Ah, there coachmen, crack your whips,
Ah, there coachmen, crack your whips,
Set the wagons rolling,
Harness all the horses;
On the way we go."

They rode through the village,
They rode through the village
And the people stared.
"Who can these men be
Who have seized the maid?"

Wyjechał w pole,	*Through the fields he rode,*
Wyjechał w pole;	*Through the fields he rode,*
Śmignął na konie.	*He cracked the whip o'er the horses,*
"Obejrzyj się dziewcze moje;	*"Look around, dear girl;*
Cy wszystko twoje?"	*Have you everything?"*

"A wszystko, wszystko,	*"O everything have I,*
A wszystko, wszystko	*O everything have I*
Co jest na wozie;	*In the wagon here.*
Zapomniałam wianka,	*Only my garland*
Srebnego pierścionka	*And my silver ring*
W izbie na stole.	*Are home upon the table.*

"Wróciłabym się,	*"O I could return,*
Wróciłabym się,	*O I could return*
Ale nie wróce,	*But that I will not do,*
Bo ja swojej pani matce	*For I'd sadden the poor heart*
Serce zasmucę."	*Of my dear mother."*

"A juz-ci to juz po wianeczku juz!	*"Gone forever is your garland,*
A juz-ci to juz po wianeczku juz!	*Gone forever is your garland.*
Kornet wity, cepek szyty	*A wreathed crown and a stitched cap*
To na ciebie przyzwoity,	*Are the symbols of your station,*
To na główkę włóz."	*Put them on your head."*

Another version begins:

Hej tam na góre	*Lo over yonder hill*
Jadą żołnierze,	*Soldiers are riding.*
Stuk, puk, stuk, puk w okienieczko,	*Tap, tap, tap, tap, on the window*
"Otwórz, otwórz, panieneczko,	*"Open, open, little maiden,*
Koniom wody daj."	*Water the horses."*

Kolberg writes that in 1845, this song, in any of its popular versions, was still used as part of the wedding festivities. Before leaving their home, the young couple fell to their knees before their parents and asked for their blessing. The assembled guests then sang this song. By 1860, the custom was not as prevalent. For variants, see Kolberg, *Lud*, I, 127; VI, Part 2, 111-112; XVIII, Part 1, 146-147; *Mazowsze*, II, Part 1, 35-37; III, 131-132; Jan Grzegorzewski, *Na Spiszu, Studya I Teksty Folklorystyczne*, p. 90.

[27] For comparative notes, see Child, *The English and Scottish Popular Ballads*, I, 22-62, where the author cites examples of the Polish versions in which the girl outwits her treacherous lover. He observes that "a ballad resembling English C-F, but with important differences, is extraordinarily diffused in Poland." Karlowicz cites eighty-nine recorded Polish versions. He disagrees with Kolberg, who attributes this ballad to the folk, for to him it is clearly the work of a clever and experienced rimer, if not poet. See Jan Karlowicz, "Systematyka Pieśni Ludu Polskiego," *Wisła*, IV, 393-418. See also Kolberg, *Mazowsze*, II, Part 2, 35; III, 274; IV, 320-321; V, 288-290; *Lud*, VI, Part 2, 168-169; XII, Part 4, 62-63; XVI, Part 1, 289-291; XIX, Part 2, 148-150; Belden, *Ballads and Songs Collected by the Missouri Folk-Lore Society*, 5-16; Gardner and Chickering, *Ballads and Songs of Southern Michigan*, 29-31. Many references to the supernatural elements in this ballad are given in Wimberly, *Folklore in the English and Scottish Ballads*, 137-138, 143, 305. He cites A. G. Gilchrist, who points out that originally the knight may have been a descendant of the water-sprite, Havmand, of the Scandinavian ballads, who disguised himself as a knight in order to marry a land maiden and drag her down to his undersea home.

[28] For other songs which use the motif of the girl who spreads her hair over her right shoulder while sitting on a rock, see Kolberg, *Lud*, III, Part 1, 265, 306, 314.

[29] For variants collected in Poland, see Kolberg, *Lud*, IV, Part 2, 51; VI, Part 2, 171; XVI, Part 1, 295; *Mazowsze*, V, 293-294. In a version sung in the Kujawy District, (*Lud*, IV, 51) the accusers ask the guilty mother to choose her form of death: burning at the stake or drowning. She answers, "I cannot float. Scatter my ashes over a field o'ergrown with darnel. Then the girls who weed the fields will sing of my fate."

[30] An anonymous songbook, *Pieśniarz*, ascribes the text to Teofil Lenartowicz (1822-1893), poet, sculptor, writer of popular airs and peasant ditties.

[31] For examples of this motif in Michigan, see Gardner and Chickering, *Ballads and Songs of Southern Michigan*, 42, 44, 52. It is also used in the ballad, *Fair Margaret and Sweet William*.

[32] St. John's Eve falls on June 23. Pagans celebrated the coming of the summer soltice with fire festivals to encourage the sun's continuity in its course in the heavens. With the coming of Christianity, the celebration not only acquired a new name in honor of St. John the Baptist, but was so modified that only faint traces of the original rite remain. In Poland, it is customary for girls to set wreaths of greens, centered with candles, afloat in the streams on St. John's Eve. The boys, standing on the opposite shore, reach for the wreaths floating toward them, thus "determining" which girls will become their brides during the coming year. The superstition that water was the abode of evil spirits slowly disappeared with the coming of Christianity. Bathing in streams and lakes before June 24 was considered unsafe, and not until the waters were blessed on that day would the early Christians venture into them. See Kolberg, *Mazowsze*, I, Part 1, 168-171 for St. John's Eve customs among the Mazovians. See Zygmunt Gloger, *Księga Rzeczy Polskich*, 450-453 for a discussion of the fire festival (*sobótki*).

[33] In folklore, the raven is the embodiment of evil prophecy and is usually an omen of approaching death. In Polish legend, the raven's young are white, but their feathers turn black as a penalty for their evil deeds. Because of the ancient belief in bird and animal souls, ballads often contain instances of talking or helpful birds and animals. See Swainson, *Folklore and Provincial Names of British Birds*, 88-92; Jan Stanisław Bystroń, *Dzieje Obyczajów w Dawnej Polsce*, I, 283-285; Wimberly, *Folk-Lore in the English and Scottish Ballads*, 44-52; James George Frazer, *The Golden Bough*, I, 197, 320; III, 34, 323-324; VIII, 221.

[34] In a twenty-seven stanza variant sung in the Kujawy District, a miller's daughter rejects a lord and is eventually beheaded by the executioner. See Kolberg, *Lud* IV, Part 2, 44. The Mazovians sing of an executioner who does not propose but throws the girl into the Danube. She swims to Danzig, comes ashore and gives thanks to God. See Kolberg, *Mazowsze* III, 285-286; V, 301-302.

[35] For variants, see Kolberg, *Mazowsze*, III, 63-64.

[36] Polish folk weddings were festivals of song, folk operas in essence. On the Sunday before the ceremony, the bride and bridesmaids met to weave garlands for the wedding party. They also decorated the whips, carts and wagons which would be used on the wedding day. The wedding staff (*rózga weselna*) was made at this time too. It consisted of seven leafy branches, the bottoms of which were woven into a staff and tied with a festive bow of colored ribbons. The leafy tops were decorated with fruit and more ribbons. During these activities, the girls sang love songs and songs appropriately describing their activities. Throughout the wedding, love songs, dance songs, singing games, as well as songs dramatizing various activities made a memorable pageantry of the occasion. This included, among others, an invitation to the guests as the bridal couple went from cottage to cottage; the claiming of the bride by her groom; her farewell to her parents, her home, the animals and orchard; the ride to church and the return; the expression of gratitude to the cook; the cook's long reply in verse, and sometimes in song; the toasts and more love songs, dance songs, singing games; the unveiling of the bride; and so forth. Much of the pageantry was disappearing during the later years of Kolberg's collecting (1857-1890). Only fragments can be seen and heard in this country now. For a detailed discussion of the folk wedding festival see Kolberg, *Lud*, I, 23-107. For variants of

No. 84, see Kolberg *Lud*, III, Part 1, 266, 287; *Mazowsze*, I, Part 1, 287-288, 232-233; III, 106, 118, 165, IV, 199.

[37] For variants, see Kolberg, *Lud*, I, 32; Bystroń, *Pieśni Ludu Polskiego*, 19.

[38] The harvest festival, a symbol of fruitfulness, is the culmination of the year's work in the fields. Late in the afternoon on the day of the festival, the girls who have helped in the fields weave a garland, singing as they work. Into this garland, which is usually shaped like a high crown, are woven the grains, fruits, nuts, and wild flowers, symbolizing the fields, orchards, and woods. Sometimes a small piece of pastry is placed at the head of the crown to represent the culinary arts. The finished wreath is placed on the head of the most skillful harvester. At sundown, she leads the group of harvesters to the home of the master, singing the harvest songs. At the gateway, hidden workers dash water on the queen and her crown, thus warding off any possibility of drought during the coming year. The landlord and his family accept the wreath and hang it on a peg in the vestibule. An exchange of gifts and speeches follows. The landlord drinks a toast to the oldest woman present; the peasant band strikes up and the master dances with the queen of the harvest, while his wife chooses the oldest man present. The villagers join in the festivities which include dancing, singing and refreshments. For variants, see Gloger, *Księga Rzeczy Polskich*, 68-70; Kolberg, *Lud*, III, Part 1, 232-233.

[39] According to the informant, there are twenty to thirty stanzas to this song. The peasants sing it vigorously as they dance the *oberek*, sometimes improvising as they whirl and stamp.

[40] The *zbójnik* is the outlaw of the mountain district of Poland. In Polish legend, Janosik, their leader, has attained the proportions of Robin Hood, robbing the rich and aiding the poor. The attire of the outlaw is rich in ornament, as if to accent the dash and color of his boldness. His dance has many characteristics of a war dance. It is performed collectively by men only, who leap into the air nimbly as they sing, brandishing hatchets. They stoop swiftly, throwing their hatchets into the air again and again, catching them with unusual dexterity. For further description of the outlaw dance, see Adam Fischer, *Lud Polski*, 197.

[41] For another version, see Kolberg, *Lud*, XIII, Part 5, 79.

[42] For another version, see Gloger, *Pieśni Dawne*, 35.

[43] At one time, beggars played an important role in the lives of village people. They were eagerly received as bringers of news. They were looked upon as authorities in religious matters, for they brought news of pilgrimages and devotions. They recited new prayers and sang new songs as they kneeled on the doorsteps of the cottages. Later their repertoire included lay songs. They popularized in song such historical events as the invasion by the Swedes, the Battle of Vienna, and the religious uprising at Thorn. They prayed over the sick and healed the ailing. They forecast crop growth and performed certain fertility rites. The beggars—cripples, soldiers, wandering sievemakers, blacksmiths, locksmiths, potters—made a formidable army. Often they were intelligent, restless, curious individuals to whom the life of the wanderer made a strong appeal. They were well organized, having their own king and their own frolics. Tradition has it that they often possessed great riches, and they used their own jargon to exclude intruders. Today, a beggar in Poland is just a beggar—nothing more. For a full discussion of the beggar, the minstrel, the pilgrim, and the gypsy in medieval Poland, see Jan Stanisław Bystroń, *Kultura Ludowa*, 101-125.

[44] Two texts are combined here. The first three stanzas are part of a well-known folksong; the fourth is taken from Wyspiański's play *Wesele*. See Stanisław Wyspiański, *Wesele*, 223-225.

[45] For variants, see Kolberg, *Lud*, IV, Part 2, 33; VI, Part 2, 129.

[46] For another version, see Kolberg, *Lud*, XIII, Part 5, 9-10.

NOTES TO "AN ANALYSIS OF THE POLISH
FOLKSONGS"

[1] Phillips Barry, Fannie Hardy Eckstrom, and Mary Winslow Smyth, *British Ballads from Maine* (New Haven: Yale University Press, 1929), p. xxi.

[2] Percy Grainger, "Impress of Personality in Unwritten Music," *The Musical Quarterly*, I (1915), 421.

[3] Definition: "Strict values of tempo are to be disregarded at caprice, the long notes stealing time from the short."—Rupert Hughes, *Music Lovers' Encyclopedia* (New York: Garden City Publishing Co., 1939), p. 671.

[4] Ignace Paderewski, "Chopin," *Poland America*, XIII (May, 1932), 200.

[5] John A. Lomax and Alan Lomax, *Our Singing Country* (New York: Macmillan Company, 1941), p. xiv.

[6] Artur Rodzinski, "Music as a Product of National Genius," *Poland*, VII (March, 1926), 149.

[7] Barry, Eckstrom, and Smyth, *British Ballads from Maine*, p. xxi.

[8] Conway Walker, *Folk Song and Dance* (New York: The Caston Institute, Inc., 1926), p. 11.

[9] Charles Heinroth, *Series of Six Radio Talks on Folk Songs* (Pittsburgh: University of Pittsburgh, 1929), pp. 28-29.

[10] Percy Goetschius, *Lessons in Music Form* (Boston: O. Ditson Company, 1904), p. 2.

[11] *Ibid.*, p. 2.

[12] Barry, Eckstrom, and Smyth, *British Ballads from Maine*, p. xxii.

APPENDIXES

A. THE EFFECTS OF ORAL TRADITION UPON THE TEXTS OF FIFTEEN VERSIONS OF "JOHN WAS WAT'RING HORSES, KATE WAS DRAWING WATER"

The following chart shows the changes which a folk ballad undergoes in its travels across a nation, and eventually across the Atlantic. Fifteen versions of "John Was Wat'ring Horses" (Child, No. 4) are herewith presented in translation.

A study of the chart will show that the theme of the ballad has not changed, but details describing the action and reaction of John and Kate are as varied as the personalities of the singers themselves. The changes also include descriptions of the travels of the pair, as well as the loot taken by John, the tribute paid Kate, and the punishment of the villain.

As Karlowicz stated ("Systematyka Pieśni Ludu Polskiego," *Wisła*, IV, 405), a folksong can be compared to an Alpine glacier, which presents no changes in its outward appearance, but which is actually changing slowly and constantly.

Jasio Konie Poił	The Setting
1	No. 1 Collected in Hamtramck, Michigan Song in present collection	John was wat'ring horses, Kate was drawing water. Johnny's heart sang gaily, Kate was far from happy.
2	No. 2 Collected in Detroit, Michigan Song in present collection	While Johnny fed his horse, Katie was drawing water.
3	No. 3 Collected in Rosciszewo, Province of Warsaw Karłowicz, p. 396	K was drawing water; J was watering his horse. J was alienating K from her father and mother.
4	No. 4 Collected in Sandomierz District, Province of Kielce Karłowicz, p. 397	J was watering horses; K was drawing water. J was persuading her to go away with him.
5	No. 5 Collected in Bronowice, Province of Lublin Karłowicz, p. 398	J was watering horses; K was drawing water. O, as J whistled, K wept.
6	No. 6 Collected in Janów District, Province of Lublin Karłowicz, p. 399	J was watering horses; K was drawing water. O, as J sang, K wept.
7	No. 7 Collected in Chełmski District, Province of Lublin Karłowicz, p. 399	J was watering horses; K was drawing water. As J sang, K wept.
8	No. 8 Collected in Leski District, Province of Lwów Karłowicz, p. 400	J came from distant lands to tempt the girls to join his family.
9	No. 9 Collected in Kraków, Province of Kraków Karłowicz, p. 401	
10	No. 10 Collected in Bohatyrowicze, Province of Białostok Karłowicz, p. 402	J was watering horses; K was drawing water. J was trying to entice K to ride away with him.
11	No. 11 Collected in Wołkowski District, Province of Białostok Karłowicz, p. 403	J was watering horses; K was drawing water. J was enticing K to go away with him.
12	No. 12 Collected in Lidzki District, Province of Nowogród Karłowicz, p. 404	J was watering horses; K was drawing water. J was coaxing K to go away with him.
13	No. 13 Collected in Rawicz, Province of Posen Kolberg, XII, 63	J was watering horses; K was drawing water. J shouted gaily, K wept.
14	No. 14 Collected in Bychawy, Province of Lublin Kolberg, XVI, 289	J was watering horses; K was drawing water. While was singing, K was weeping.
15	No. 15 Collected in Chomentów, Province of Kielce Kolberg, XIX, 148	J went to water his horses. He saw K. He began to tempt her.

THE TEMPTATION	THE OBSTACLE
"Katie, why the tears, dear? Why the lamentation? Choose the road, dear Katie, I will take you with me."	"Gladly would I travel, Nought would stop me, Johnny, If my mamma had not Locked up all my fin'ry."
Johnny was urging Kate To wander off with him.	
"Little K, take gold and silver so that my grey horse may have something to carry."	"I would take as much as I could, but mother has the keys to the new chest."
"Wander, K, wander. Take enough silver so that my black horse will have enough to carry."	"How can I, when it is not in my power? Mother has hidden it in the new chamber."
"Take enough gold and silver, K, so that my black horse will have something to carry."	
"Take enough gold and silver, K, O, that my little horse may have something to carry."	
The beautiful girl was easily persuaded. She ordered that her black horse be harnessed.	
"O, K, go into the new chamber. Fill the bags with gold and silver, K."	"It is unthinkable that I should take it myself! Mother has hidden the keys to the new room."
"K, take enough gold and silver so that my black horse will have something to carry."	
	"It is not right that I should go with you and take my mother's keys with me."
Several stanzas which were included in this version by the Lublin folk were omitted by Kolberg in his collection.	*See left side.*
"Little K, take enough gold and silver, then my black horse will, O carry it."	

1

2

3

4

5

6

7

8   "Servants, my little servants, you who are most faithful, harness those horses which are most willing to go."   The horses neighed and shied, for they knew of the girl' coming misfortune.

9

10

11

12

13

14   *Several stanzas which were included in this version by the Lublin folk were omitted by Kolberg in his collection.*   *See left side.*

15

PLAN FOR THEFT	DECEPTION OF MOTHER
"Why not tell your mother That you have a headache? Then, indeed, she'll let you Rest inside the new room."	And so Katie's mamma Thought that she was ailing, But her Kate was trav'ling All night long with Johnny.
"Why not tell your mother Your head is sore with pain? You will then get the keys To the padlocked storeroom."	And so her mamma thought Katie was resting there, But Kate was wand'ring Over the world with John.
"K, say your head aches; then you will get the keys to the new chest."	Mamma thought K was sleeping, but K was wandering over the world with J.
	Mamma thought little K was sleeping, but K was wandering with J all night.
"I ask you, K, does your head ache? Your mother will give you the keys to the new room."	Mother thought K was sleeping, but K was wandering all night with J.
"Little K, say that your little head aches. O, your mother will admit you to the new room."	Mother thought K was sleeping. O, K had wandered into the world with J.
"Tell mother your head aches. She will return the keys to the new room."	Mamma thought K was sleeping, but K was wandering all night with J.
"K, say that your head aches. Your mother will admit you to the new room."	Mamma thought little K was sleeping, but she was wandering all night with J.
"K, say, 'My little head aches'; then mamma will admit you into the new room."	Mamma thought K was sleeping, but K wandered throughout the entire world with J.
"K, say that your little head aches; then mamma will give you keys to the new room."	Mamma thought K was sleeping, but K was wandering all night with J.
"Girl, say that your little head aches, that you will go to rest in the new room."	Mamma thought that little K was sleeping, but K had left long before with J.
"Do not cry, K. Say your little head aches; then mamma will give you the keys to the new room."	
Several stanzas which were included in this version by the Lublin folk were omitted by Kolberg in his collection.	*See left side.*
	Mamma thought K was sleeping, but K was wandering all night with J.

	First Stop, Real or Implied	J's First Command
1	And at last they wandered To a forest dreary.	"Loosen here, my Katie, Your fair braids in good time."
2	They had not gone too far, Just a short way from home.	"Katie let us return Home to your cottage now."
3	White sandy stretch. "Let us rest, handsome lad." (K.)	"Not for this, not for this did you wander, that you should rest now."
4	Dark forest	"Take off your French finery."
5	Dark woods	"O, let down your braids to your waist."
6	Dense forest	"O let down your braid betimes."
7	White birch grove	"Spread your down featherbeds, K."
8	After a speechless ride, K asks, "Where is our family?"	"Do not ask about your family, you fool, for you will soon be among the reeds in the Danube." (J snatches the golden rings.)
9	Black forest. "Father, mother, she is no longer ours." (singer.)	
10	White birch grove	"K, return to your family!"
11	White birch grove	"K, return to your family!"
12	They pass mountains and forests.	"Take off your golden girdle, youthful K."
13	A forest	"Disrobe, K, so I may have your costly finery!"
14	*Several stanzas which were included in this version by the Lublin folk were omitted by Kolberg in his collection.*	*See left side.*
15	A wood	"K, return to your mother's home."

K's Reaction	Second Stop
"Not for this did Mamma Comb and plait my tresses, Now to drag and snarl them Over all these brambles."	When at last they wandered To that long and wide bridge,
"I have not wandered forth Only to go back now, Only to bring sorrow To my dear parents now."	
	Beaten road
"Take, take my corals from around my throat. Buy yourself some horses in Warsaw, J. Take, take my silken skirt. Buy yourself a stone mansion, J. Take, take all my finery. Buy yourself a home in Berlin, J."	
"O my mother did not sleep nights, but combed and braided my hair."	Beaten road
"I did not braid my hair that I should now loosen it and O, drag it over the branches."	Beaten road
"Not for this did I go with you, J, that I should now spread my featherbeds in the birch grove."	Dark forest
	Field
"Not for this did I wander away that I should now return and sadden the hearts of my father and my little mother."	Dark spring
"I did not ride away that I should now return. My mother would only complain."	Grey sea
"You have no right to ask that I should throw off the beautiful purchases of my little mother."	
"I did not come here to disrobe and waste the night with you, you scoundrel."	High bridge
"I did not take them with me that I should forfeit them. O my mother has already forgotten me!"	Black forest
"The world would have to turn topsy-turvy, J, ere I would return to my mother."	Tavern

J's Second Command	K's Reaction
1	
2	
3 "K, take off, take off your golden rings."	And she removed them, yet did not remove them. "O God, have mercy, God Almighty."
4	
5 "O take off your silver rings, K."	"O my dear brother did not sleep nights, but rode off in search of these rings in Krakow."
6 "O, K, take off, take off, those silver rings."	"I did not accept them that I should now remove them and hand them over to you."
7 "Loosen your braids to your waist!"	"Not for this did I go with you, J, that I should now loosen my braids in the forest."
8	
9 "Disrobe, K, that I may take your costly garments."	
10 "Disrobe and give me your costly finery!" (J takes K's golden rings and silk stockings.)	
11 "Return to your mother, K!"	"I did not ride away that I should now return. Rather would I wander on with you, J."
12 "Throw off those golden rings, youthful K!"	
13	
14 "K, loosen your hair to the waist!"	"I did not braid my hair that I should loosen it now O my mother has already forgotten me."
15	"Rest, my dear little feet." (K.)

Danube River   "On your guard, K! Which of us will die now?"

Dense hazel grove   "K, return to your family!"

Deep Danube

Forest   "Girl, remove your apparel!"

Wide plain   "Look back, K. Can you find your way to your mother?"

Danube River   "If you wish to swim this Danube, K, remove your dresses, dear little K."

Dark forest   "Return to your mother's home, youthful K."

White birch grove   "Spread your down featherbeds, K."

Danube River   "K, do you see this deep Danube? Your little grey eyes will soon be floating there."

1

2

3

4

5

6   "I did not go off, that I should now return, that I should   Black Danube
add to the grief of my dear mother."

7

8   Wood

9   "The world would have to turn topsy-turvy, ere I return   Green grass
to mamma."

10

11

12   "You have no right to ask that I return, after I have   Wide Danube
squandered my dear mamma's fortune."

13

14   "Not for this did I take them, that I should now spread   Green grove
them. O my mother has already forgotten me."

15   "Dear J, sell my cotton finery and buy, buy yourself a
stone mansion. Dear J, sell my golden finery and buy,
buy yourself two city dwellings. Dear J, sell my wreath
of rue and buy, buy yourself a castle in Krakow."

"O here, here you must meditate, K!"

"Remove your satins, Girl!"

"K, remove your little wreath from your head."   "I will not remove it. My dear little mother wove it. Sadly she wove each little blossom into it."

"O look, little K! what glistens so whitely. I would tell you, K, but do not be frightened. Here lie my nine wives, and you are the tenth."

"O my little K, nothing will help you. You must swim the swift lake."

	Fifth Stop	J's Fifth Command
1		
2		
3		
4		
5		
6		
7		
8		
9		
10		
11		
12		
13		
14	Swift Danube	"Look, K, which of us will perish now?"
15		

Johnny threw poor Katie
Deep into the Danube.

He seized her tiny hand,
He caught her 'round the waist,
He threw her, he threw her
Into the deep Danube.

And lo! her pretty wreath
Was caught around a pole.
"I did not cast you off, Only to save you now,
Only to untangle Your garland from the pole."

He took her by her little sides. He threw her, he threw her into the deep Danube.

Her apron dangled on an oaken pole.

He caught her, he caught her lightly by the sides. He threw her, he threw her into the deep Danube.

He caught her by her slender sides. He threw her into the deep Danube.

O her apron tangled on a pole.

He caught her by her slender arms. He caught her by her sides. He threw her, he threw her into the deep Danube.

He caught her by her sides and threw her into the deep Danube.

And he grasped her, he grasped her by her slender sides, and he threw her, he threw her into the deep Danube.

Her little apron curled around a stump. J drew his sword and slashed it in three.

J caught K by her snow-white sides. J threw K into the deep Danube.

"Swim, K, swim from side to side. There are four maidens; you will be the fifth." (J.)

And then he caught dear little K by her snow-white sides and he threw her, poor thing, into the deep Danube.

J caught K by her slender sides and he threw her, he threw her into that deep Danube.

"Swim, K, swim from side to side. Here already lie four, and you will be the fifth."

And J threw K into the deep pool.

"Why should I have come here just to save you now? Your little braids must drag you to the bottom."

He caught her, he caught her by her slender sides. O he threw her, he threw her into that deep Danube.

O she tangled her apron around a pole.

Little J caught K by her sides; he threw her, he threw her into the deep Danube.

K's apron became tangled around a pole.

K's Plea for Aid	Arrival of Brothers
1 "Anchor me, O fair braids, / To the water's bottom. / Undeserving am I / Of such fate from Johnny."	High upon a mountain / Katie's brother saw this; / Down he slid to Katie / On a silken cable.
2 "Save me, my dear Johnny, / Save me, my heart of hearts."	
3 "Save me, J, my heart's delight."	And her brother saw her from a high mountain. He dropped down to her on a silken rope.
4	Her brother heard her from a high mountain. He dropped down to his sister on a silken rope.
5 "O save me, dear J; save me, my falcon."	Poor K looked up toward the mountain; her brother was sliding down a silken rope.
6	
7	From a high mountain her brothers saw her. "Make ready your ropes, fishermen," they said.
8	
9	
10 "Save me, J, save me. What is wrong with you? My little braid cannot reach bottom."	
11 "Anchor me, anchor me to the bottom, O braid. Perhaps I am not worthy of this death as yet."	
12 Little K swims, little K sinks. "Save me, dear J, for I have loved you."	And when her brother heard her from a high mountain, he slid to his sister down a silken rope.
13	
14	
15 "O save me, save me, dear J, my falcon."	

AID FROM STRANGERS	THE WHITE ROCK
Fishermen were nearby Dragging nets of fish in, And they dragged fair Katie From the wat'ry bottom.	And they placed her gently On a glist'ning white rock,
Netweavers, fishermen, Make your nets ready now. And beautiful Katie Drag from the water now.	
The fishermen cast their nets. They brought innocent K to shore.	And she sat upon a white rock.
The fishermen, fishermen cast their nets, and brought beautiful sister to shore.	She sat upon a white rock.
The fishermen, fishermen cast their nets and brought beautiful K to shore.	And she sat upon a white rock.
The fishermen cast their nets. They brought beautiful K to shore.	
There were fishermen; they cast their nets. They brought beautiful K to shore.	K sat upon a white rock.
The fishermen caught her. Lifeless they brought her.	
The fishermen, fishermen, while they were fishing, got miserable K from the water.	
Out of a mansion there came a servant. "Deliver yourself to the care of the Virgin." No prayer had she uttered; in her mind she had thought it, when K to the shore was delivered.	

	K's Hair	The Moral and the Ballad Ghost
I	And they spread her tresses Over her right shoulder.	"Less I grieve for you, Kate, Then for your lost garland. You have loved unwisely This roue, your sweetheart." (Brother's words.)
2		
3	She spread her hair over her right shoulder.	"Take heed, maidens and you wives. What ill luck to leave your father and mother! As many kernels as a barley stalk has, so much evil and greed does each man possess. As much wool as a little white lamb has, so much virtue and humility does each maid possess."
4	She combed her braid over her right shoulder.	She came to the church. She stood in the doorway. She wept as she looked upon the maidens. "Take heed, maidens and you, wives, how unwise it is to leave your father and mother."
5		Her mother went to the church. She stood in the doorway. She wept as she looked upon the maidens. "Do you see, maidens and you wives? Such is the fate of those who leave their father and mother."
6	She spread her golden hair over her right shoulder.	She went to the church. She stood in the doorway. She wept as she looked upon the maidens. "Take heed, maidens and you wives. O how sad it is to leave your father and mother."
7		
8		
9		"Take heed, maidens and you, children. How sad it is to roam without your father and mother."
10	Spreading her hair over her right shoulder.	"Take heed, maidens and you, young wives. What ill luck to wander away from your mother."
11		
12		"I shall go to the church. I shall stand behind the pews. As I see each maiden, I shall weep freely. Take heed, maidens and wives! How sad it is to leave your father and mother."
13		
14		She went to the church. She stood in the doorway. She wept freely as she looked upon the altar.
15		And so little K wrote letters that her family would come to the funeral. She came to the church; she knelt at the door. She glanced at the altar; she wept freely. (Moralizes as in Version 9.)

TRIBUTE TO K	PUNISHMENT FOR J
Poor dear wretched Katie, Four bells toll her sad fate. Poor dear wretched Katie To her grave is lowered.	But that villain, Johnny! Horses four pursue him. But that villain, Johnny! From a rope he dangles.
For K, dear little K, they toll the bells; for K, dear little K, they play the organ.	And a hundred horses pursue J, and they hang J, the scoundrel, beyond the woods.
For beautiful K they toll four bells.	And J, the scoundrel, is pursued by four horses.
And so dear little K floats here and there. The people are grieving; her parents are grieving.	
And now all the bells sing for little K, and now all the bells toll for little K.	J, the evil one, is chopped into mincemeat. J, the evil one, is pursued by a hundred horses.
The father and mother grieve for little K. All the bells toll for youthful little K.	A black raven caws for J, the thief, and three horses pursue J, the thief.
The organs play for miserable K. People sing over the grave of miserable K. They lower miserable K into her grave.	A hundred horses pursue J, the scoundrel. People chop J, the scoundrel, into poppyseeds, and they scatter him with the wind.
Four bells toll for poor K. They lower poor K into the grave.	Six horses gallop after treacherous J, and treacherous J is chopped into poppyseeds.
And now golden bells toll for dear little K. And now the organs play for dear little K.	And a hundred horses pursue J, the dog. And the horses tear apart J, the dog.

1

2

3

4

5

6

7

8

9

10 They found J in a Krakow marketplace. He was leading
another in a lavender wreath.

11

12

13

14 And they found him in a Warsaw market place. A maid
in a lavender wreath was following him.

15

B. INFORMANTS

Adam Bartosz: Born in southern Poland in 1894, where early in life he became familiar with the lore of the surrounding country. His education, begun in Poland, was continued at the University of Baltimore after his arrival in the United States in 1913. He lived in Baltimore and in St. Louis before settling in Stevens Point, Wisconsin, where he has been editor of *Gwiazda Polarna* and *Rolnik*, two newspapers.

Mrs. Ferdinand Chenik: Born in Przemyśl, but came to Winnipeg, Canada, with her parents when she was three years old. As a nurse, her duties took her to Banff, Alberta, Los Angeles, and Detroit. It was in her early years in Winnipeg, however, that she was introduced to Polish folksongs, and a few of them still remain in her memory.

Mrs. Sophia Dziob: Born in Nisko, near Krakow. In her early childhood, her parents moved to the village of Tomaszowce. It was here that she learned many of the songs which she sang for the present collection. Whenever the young people met, there was sure to be song, she said. Her ambition at that time was to learn each new song after hearing it once, an ambition which she easily realized. She sang at work in the fields and in and about her cottage, as well as at the village social gatherings. After her arrival in Passaic, New Jersey, in 1912, she learned other songs from her Polish friends in America. Eventually, her repertoire included the sentimental lyrics which she heard more and more frequently, especially after she settled in Hamtramck in 1927. She contributed her songs with an appreciation which is always welcome to a collector. She sang her songs without apology for their simple origins, pointing out a gracefully turned expression here and rustic humor there. She often said, while she was dictating the words, that the unadorned simplicity and sincerity of language could not be matched in the sentimental lyrics which are so popular now. She casually broke the melodies and texts into patterns and pointed out the peasants' use of certain formulas. She defined terms not generally known, and described their cultural background. At the time of the recording, Mrs. Dziob was a widow in her early forties, working in a Detroit restaurant.

Frank First: Born in Detroit in 1912. His mother, born in Sonina, and his father, born in Gorlice near the Carpathian Mountains, lived in Łancut for some time after their marriage. When they sailed for America, they left one daughter behind with relatives. Many of the songs which Mr. First knows today were learned from his sister, who joined her family later. Most of the songs, however, came from the long repertoire of his mother and grandmother.

Mrs. Jozefa Kochanowska: Born near Warsaw. After the invasion of Poland in 1939, she left for England with other refugees and remained there for ten months. In September 1940 she arrived in the United States. She was invited to join a small group of Detroit friends who were meeting for a "collector of Polish folksongs."

Mrs. John Krupski: Born in Kornik, Poland, in 1880. When she was about two years old, her parents came to the United States, where they settled in Buffalo. Much that Mrs. Krupski can contribute in the way of Polish lore, she learned from her mother, whose fund of song and proverb seemed inexhaustible. She also learned from a group of young women with whom she worked and associated during her youth. After her marriage, Mrs. Krupski settled in Detroit in 1912.

Mrs. Bernice Mochocka: Born in Dziektażewo, Poland. She came to the United States in 1910, first to East Hampton, Massachusetts, then to Toledo, and finally, in 1929, to Detroit. Like Mrs. Kochanowska, she joined a small group of singers who contributed folksongs for the present collection. One of the "little beggar" songs had actually been sung to her by a wandering singer when she lived in Dziektażewo.

Mrs. Helen Poplawska: Born in Narol, Poland. She came to America in 1911 and settled in Detroit. She visited Poland a few years before the outbreak of World War II and has contributed articles to the *Dziennik Polski* on her impressions of that visit. In the interest of the present collection, she joined the group of singers at the home of Mrs. Szczepanik.

Mrs. Alexandra Szczepanik: Born in Bircze, Poland. She came to this country in 1920 and settled in Detroit. During my search for folksongs, Mrs. Szczepanik invited friends for a songfest and recording session.

Mrs. Victoria Zdziebko: Born in Turek, Province of Kalisz, Poland in 1887. After her marriage, she served as matchmaker at folk weddings "about seventy-five times." After coming to Detroit in 1922, she has prepared food for many a folk wedding feast. When the occasion arises, she sings the traditional ceremonial songs.

C. BIBLIOGRAPHY

Belden, H. M., ed., *Ballads and Songs Collected by the Missouri Folklore Society*. Columbia, Mo.: University of Missouri, 1940.

Bystroń, Jan Stanisław. *Dzieje Obyczajów W Dawnej Polsce*. Warszawa: 1932.

———— *Kultura Ludowa*. Warszawa: 1947.

———— *Pieśni Ludu Polskiego*. Kraków: 1924.

Child, Francis James. *The English and Scottish Popular Ballads*. 5 vols.; Boston: Houghton, Mifflin and Company, 1892-1898.

Elton, Oliver. "Epilogue to Pan Tadeusz." *Slavonic and East European Review, XIX* (1939-40), 1-13 (*Slavonic Yearbook*, VI).

Fischer, Adam. *Lud Polski*. Lwów: 1926.

Frazer, James George. *The Golden Bough*. 12 vols.; New York: The Macmillan Company, 1935.

Gardner, Emelyn Elizabeth, and Geraldine Jenks Chickering. *Ballads and Songs of Southern Michigan*. Ann Arbor: University of Michigan Press, 1939.

Gloger, Zygmunt. *Encyklopedja Staropolska*. 4 vols.; Warszawa: 1903.

———— *Księga Rzeczy Polskich*. Kraków: 1896.

———— *Pieśni Dawne*. Warszawa: 1905.

———— *Zwyczaje I Pieśni Doroczne*. Warszawa: 1898.

Grzegorzewski, Jan. *Na Spiszu, Studya I Teksty Folklorystyczne*. Lwów: 1919.

Karłowicz, Jan. "Systematyka Pieśni Ludu Polskiego." *Wisła*, IV (1890), 393-425.

Kolberg, Oskar. *Lud*. 22 vols.; Warszawa: 1857-1867. Kraków: 1871-1890.

———— *Mazowsze*. 5 vols.; Kraków: 1888-1890.

Sembrzycki, Jan. "Przyczyniki do Charakterystyki Mazurów Pruskich." *Wisła*, III (1889), 584-85.

Swainson, Charles. *The Folk Lore and Provincial Names of British Birds*. London: E. Stock, 1886.

Wimberly, Lowry Charles. *Folklore in the English and Scottish Ballads*. Chicago: University of Chicago Press, 1928.

Wyspiański, Stanisław. *Wesele*. Krakow: 1916.

INDEXES

A. POLISH TITLES

B. ENGLISH TITLES

The manuscript was edited by Alexander Brede and the book was designed by William A. Bostick.

Monotype Baskerville, designed by John Baskerville between 1750 and 1758, is the type face.

This volume is printed on Warren's Olde Style Antique White Wove and bound in Bancroft's

Kennett Cloth over boards. Manufactured in the United States of America.